THE
MANY KINDS
OF *GLEE*

*A Second Book of Short Stories and Poems
for The World, from My Mind.*

KINGSLEY C. NURSE

So…once again, this too, is my *own* original work. Same as before, you can't use it without my permission. Right? Since I wrote….you know what? You already know the whole schpeel…blah blah…copyright…blah blah.

Printed in the United States of America
First Printing 2020
First Edition 2020

ISBN: 978-1-7351542-2-0
10 9 8 7 6 5 4 3 2 1

Other Books by Kingsley C. Nurse:

The Many Minds of Me: A Book of Short Stories and Poems for the World, from My Mind

KINGSLEY C. NURSE

Thanks:

To God. For giving me a chance to see the world, and express the Glee that I find...

And thanks to all my readers, for without you, I would not have anyone to share my stories or poems with.

For:

My Precious Mother, whom, above all else, would laugh at what I wrote.

This Book is Dedicated:

To all who recognize the joy of laughter, and the value of always striving to be happy. For there was a time, where people could not openly express their joy and happiness. To those who are happy among us, and to those who understand the necessity of it, may you always feel fulfilled, contented and gleefully happy, like the chickens.

Table of Contents

Foreword

Dearest Reader, It's me again!

Hi again! I thank you once more, truthfully and honestly, for looking at my second book. If you haven't already, please check out my first book: ***"The Many Minds of Me: A Book of Short Stories and Poems for The World, from My Mind"***.

You should read it, it's really good (end first book plug).

This book is an extension of the first, with some continued serious themes, but this time the book is meant to be *mostly* lighthearted and fun.

Oh, by the way, I wrote *this* book naked. Yup. That's right, *nude*. Go ahead, let your mind form a mental picture, and *envision* the horror. Picture the horror of my butt-cheeks pressed against my leather sofa. My *clean* leather sofa.

Does this world have enough happiness? I don't know. What I do know is that we need more people to appreciate the concept of fun and jokes and all-around glee. We should not take ourselves so seriously. There are times that demand our seriousness, for this world is not all roses and lavender. Times are tough and will continue to be. Pain is ever-present, and it will continue to be here for now.

But this does not mean that we should be overcome by such things. God gave us the ability to laugh and be happy for a reason. A very good reason. He understood that we humans need it. In truth, we can't live without it. So while you read, try to be amused at some of the themes in the book, then, envision yourself being happy.

I hope you truly enjoy, but more so, as you read, I hope you are at least slightly amused.

You know, *here and there.*

From my mind, *gleefully* to yours,

-Kingsley

Part I

The Fulfilling Short Stories

"Perhaps, lick the office door three times, then run around with my necktie tied to my left ear and jiggle my right toe while reciting America the beautiful…wait no, no. That would be too dangerous. People might like that too much. Or perhaps, I could go full-on weird freak, and mix some milk with orange juice. Yeah, I might do that. That's some sick twisted business right there. Off the rails up in this *bizniz*. Mix orange juice with milk. Yeah. That's right. You like that, huh? You like that, you sick milk-curdling bastard?"

-From, *Weird Request Day*

Introduction (The Fulfilling Short Stories)

I simply cannot express how much I love writing short stories. There is truly no other medium I find better, to express my ideas and thoughts, all while seeking to provide a lesson for the reader to discover and enjoy. The style is simple, yet brilliant. This medium, in its simplicity, favors and takes into consideration, the reader's time and allows the reader to intelligently garner respect and empathy for the characters and protagonists in the story, even though the characters have only been introduced to you and given key lines of backstory needed, in less than a few thousand words.

I truly wish more people embraced the short story as much as they embrace a Novel or other alternative long form work. There are simply so many amazing stories to be told, all within easily digestible chunks of prose. Sure, you can get wrapped up in the enticing world of a Novel, and spend your days fantasizing of the world built within; but the same can be said for the short story. The more I read short stories, the more I want to read. For me, it's like a never-ending quest to gain the lessons of fellow creative writers, as they leave you their personal gems and treasures to discover and appreciate.

I have already written a long introduction, explaining my love of short stories and the defense of the medium in my first book, *"The Many Minds of Me: A Book of Short Stories and Poems for The World, from My Mind"*, so I don't wish to repeat that argument here again, as that would be somewhat redundant. Instead, I would like to wish you many hours of enjoyment as you read my stories, and may you never forget the lessons I sought to expound on, within them. I truly hope you have much fun reading my ideas, as I truly and sincerely enjoyed writing each and every single one for you.

The Amazing Choice

"A man makes a choice to venture for what he wants, but time plays tricks and offers cruel taunts. He will have to choose in this realistic state, for things are not as they seem, in this sudden twist of fate."

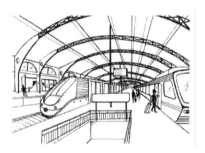

After speaking to Julie, I hung up the phone, and despite my initial dismay at how things went, I was deeply glad and relieved to know that I had made it out, somehow, without signing my rights away. I was still a little worried, as I wondered if that prolific writer would still try to steal or use my work. I shuddered at the thought that there were probably many new and naïve authors and writers, who, excited for an opportunity, probably signed away the rights to their successful stories that might have gone on to make them some money or garner a little popularity.

I told myself to always be careful signing contracts from now on, no matter what it was for. I then continued heading towards the train station to catch my train.

Once on the train, I took a window seat a few aisles down from the door and put my bag next to me in the seat adjacent. There was an excerpt from a poem, posted above the opposite seat across from me that said: *"Your dreams are the hidden reality of your mind. Stay there to live the treasures you seek to find."* It was written by *Kingsley C. Nurse.* Whoever he is, he sure is an amazing poet. I read it and thought it was a cute little piece of poetry. Deep, but very relatable. I told myself that I would love to meet a poet like him one day.

As the train began to move, I felt somewhat sleepy, so I decided to bend my head and take a short nap while riding the train home. I had woken up early that morning, and the train ride was about an hour and a half since it was the local, so I figured it was a good time to catch up on some sleep.

I nodded my head and drifted off to the drone of the moving train.

At the next station, there was a slight screech on the track, where the wheel touches a rusty part, so it jolted me awake. My mind doesn't allow me to sleep soundly while traveling in public, and any loud sound will wake me up enough to make me at least look up and check things out before nodding my head to go back to sleep.

That's when I saw her.

She was young but extremely pretty. For some reason, she looked so familiar, like I knew her. She came into the train and sat at the seat across from mine, but no one sat next to her. I was at my end of the aisle, at the window seat, and she was at the opposite end of the same aisle, at her window seat. The doors closed, and the train continued to move.

I took one look at her, and she was so pretty, that I sort of woke up. She had short curly hair, and a very nice, innocent smile. I thought she must not have been from around the area, or maybe visiting a friend.

She was writing in what looked like a diary or a notebook. She had a pencil. She would stop, think about something, then jot it down on paper, then stop again, and erase it. She kept doing this. I became very interested. I was a shy guy, and I usually didn't have enough courage to approach women, and I was still very much shocked about what had happened earlier, so I kinda felt that maybe I shouldn't.

But after another few minutes had passed; I couldn't help but stare at this gorgeous, cute girl. She was working so hard on what she was writing, so I felt a kindred spirit with her. After all, I knew what that was like. I wrote short stories and was aspiring to one day publish my book as well. Perhaps she was writing a story or a novel?

This gave me courage, as I too, being a writer, I felt like we might have some things in common, so I gathered my courage and decided to just go for it. If she wasn't interested or didn't want to be bothered, then at least the day couldn't get any worse. I waved in her direction, and she looked up at me.

"Excuse me, miss. Hi, I see you were writing there and I got a little curious. I'm also a writer too. Are you writing a story?"

"Hi, well no, actually it's a song."

"Oh really? That sounds nice, so you're a songwriter?"

"Well, I suppose you can say that. I'm a struggling singer."

"Oh, that's amazing! So you are writing your own songs?"

"Yeah. I'm not having any luck though. It's harder than it looks."

"Oh I know how that goes, trust me. Sometimes inspiration comes, and sometimes, it's like you hit a wall. Would you like some help? I'm actually pretty good! I just won a writing competition as well."

I got somewhat excited that I was carrying a conversation with this pretty young girl. She looked at her book and then looked at me, and smiled at me and said sure.

"Do you mind if I join you?" I asked. *I was feeling rather confident and wanted to get a bit closer to her.*

"I mean, if that's ok with you?"

"Sure, why not. You can sit next to me. You're not some crazy guy, right?"

I laughed. "No, of course not. Would you like my ID?" I jokingly said.

"What will that prove? You could still be crazy, you know." She was smiling, and I could tell she was teasing me.

"Well, I promise I won't hurt you. You have my writer's word."

At that, she smiled and said that since I was a fellow writer, she would trust me. I got up and moved over to her end of the aisle, and now I was sitting next to her in the aisle seat, and she was sitting at the window seat.

"So my new writer friend, do you only write now for a living, or is this just a hobby for you until you strike it big?" She asked.

"Well, I'm still in college, but I want to finish my degree, and be a writer full time. I don't write horror or anything, but I will be the next Stephen King. You watch."

She laughed at my proclamations and delusions of grandeur.

"Sure you will buddy."

She was sooo sweet! She came off very genuine and kind. I could tell she was down to earth, innocent and gentle. I became more interested in her and wanted to know her name, but I got somewhat nervous to ask her.

"So my name is Kalvin, what's your name my struggling singer friend, whom I met on this slow train today. Well, not that I mind it, because I'm enjoying myself, but it's still kinda slow. Plus I still have like an hour to my destination, so it's cool and…"

"It's Jolina. Nice to meet you, Kal."

She instantly saw that I was nervous and was blabbering and she mercifully put me out of my misery. She was really kind. Some people don't notice these things, but I do. She didn't have to stop me. She could have let me continue to blabber and make a fool out of myself. I appreciated how kind and humble she was. I smiled at her.

She smiled back and we shook hands.

"So Jolina, what are you working on?"

"Well, it's a song about love, but not willing to wait for it. The song is meant to say that instead of waiting for love to come in the future, you should embrace the love that's in front of you right now."

"Oh, that's amazing Jolina! That's an excellent idea for a song. Too many people sing about waiting for the love of their lives when there are people right there in front of them who can make them happy. Plus opportunities like that don't come around often. You should always choose to seize the opportunity to be happy."

"Yeah, that's right. Hey, you just gave me an idea for the second part of the song."

"See? I'm glad that I could be of service to you Jolina! Heheh, I can't sing, but I can certainly be an inspiration!"

"Yes, you are, you seem to be working out well, my dear new writer friend."

I smiled at her again. I looked in her eyes and wondered how I could have gotten so lucky to stumble across and meet such a sweet, kind girl. I knew I wanted to talk to her more.

"So, Kal, tell me more about you. What are some things you like to do when you're not writing?"

* * * * *

As we rode the train, we talked and talked. She told me all about her family, and how she was singing since she was a little girl. We both talked about our upbringing. We talked about how overprotective parents can be, and we talked about our dreams and goals, and our heartfelt desires. We seemed to connect pretty well, and we were both getting very comfortable with each other.

As the train kept moving, we came close to my stop, about three stations away. An announcement came over the air that someone wasn't feeling too well, and so the train would stop to get them some medical help. This happens quite often, as people get motion sickness, so I didn't think anything of it.

I was enjoying my conversation with Jolina so much, that I thanked God for the extra time to sit and talk with this amazing girl. We had talked and laughed for a good few more minutes, so I wanted to close the deal. I didn't want to lose contact with her, as eventually, my train ride would come to an end. I also didn't want to ask her where she was going, as I didn't want to come off creepy. I figured asking for her number would be ok.

"So, I don't know how long more we have to ride together, but I would love to keep talking to you. Could I maybe get your number? I can call you sometime."

"Oh, sorry Kal! I don't have a personal phone for myself right now. Well, it's more like my mom doesn't want me to have one. She said she doesn't want men calling me without her knowledge. I do have a landline phone at home though. I can give you my home phone number if that's ok with you?"

"Sure, I don't mind at all."

"Ok great, it is 263..."

The train conductor made an announcement over the air at the same time, so I missed the last few digits. I turned my ear to listen to the full announcement and then planned to ask Jolina to repeat the number when the announcement was over. It was a normal message letting all the passengers know that the train would be pulling off in a few minutes.

For some reason, as the message finished coming over the broadcast, I looked up and saw something I couldn't believe was possible. Someone had walked into the train as the doors remained open. It was someone I would never expect to see in a million years, riding a train. I simply couldn't believe it.

It was my favorite singer and celebrity, the same singer I saw this morning, walking into the train. It was her. I could never mistake her signature look anywhere. I was shocked. I had seen her walking with her boyfriend earlier, but now, here she was, sitting on the train with me! She was wearing shades, but I still recognized her. I wondered what in the world was she doing riding the train. Didn't celebrities get driven around? Wait, wasn't it kind of dangerous? Did she even know where she was going?

All these thoughts went through my head. As the announcement finished, I turned to Jolina, now excited, and completely forgot to ask her to repeat the remaining few digits.

"Jolina, do you know who that lady sitting a few rows up is?" I whispered to her, excited as hell.

"I don't think I've ever seen her, no. Who is she?"

"It's my favorite singer!" I whispered back. *"It's Jo Jo Felix! She's a huge celebrity!"*

"Oh, that's funny. Is that her real name? I've never heard of her."

"Yes, that's her real name, but really? Everyone's heard of her! She is amazing! You would love her music!"

"Really? Oh ok. Wait, why is she riding the train? Don't celebrities have to be careful?"

"Well, some still do take public transportation. Some celebrities feel like it's a way to stay human and grounded and remember that they are just like everyone else. I actually think that it is a noble thing to do. I do agree it could get dangerous sometimes, so they should try to hide a little bit."

Jolina was looking at me as I grinned ear to ear talking about my favorite singer. It seemed to make her slightly jealous that I was not completely focused on her as much anymore.

"Well, if I made it big as her, I would still ride the train sometimes too."

"You would?" I replied.

"Sure, I like the train, and I would probably just wear shades like her and stay discreet."

"What would you do if people recognize you?" I asked.

"Well, I would want to greet my fans, but as you said, it would be too dangerous, so if too many people started noticing me, I would get off the train and leave."

"Oh ok, yeah that's smart. Then you could just run and catch a taxi and disappear."

"Yeah, that's probably what I would do."

"Ok sure, yeah."

I was so focused on Ms. Felix, that I didn't hear what Jolina had to say. Everything drowned out from my view. I just wanted to walk up to Ms. Felix and say: *"Hi, I'm a huge fan. It's an honor to meet you!"*

Jolina saw that I had essentially stopped talking to her for the past two minutes, and as such, started trying to have another conversation with me. She asked me if I had any thoughts on songs about your dreams. Like the dreams you have when you sleep.

I told her I didn't, and brushed her off, and started thinking about how to approach Ms. Felix, sitting only a few seats ahead of me. The train jolted forward, and it started moving again. I was now only a few stations away from my stop. By this time, I was desperate and had forgotten all about poor sweet Jolina.

I got up and started walking slowly toward Ms. Felix. As I got to about a seat away, someone shouted out that they recognized Ms. Felix. Everyone turned around, and people began getting up and looking and started asking about where she was.

The train was pulling into the next station, and as the doors opened, I approached Ms. Felix. As I went to say hi, she jumped up and quickly walked off the train. I wanted to follow her, but I knew that was essentially stalking, so I said "Ah!" and stood by the door and watched her, as she quickly headed down the stairs. She turned to look at me, stopped for a brief second and pulled down her shades, then pulled them back up, walked further down, and disappeared.

As I watched her walk away, I suddenly remembered Jolina. I turned around and looked towards her direction, but I didn't see her. I walked back to our seat, and she was gone. She had left. No trace of her was left. Nothing. I don't think she got up and walked out of the train because I would have spotted her. I sat back down on my seat and was slightly confused. Did she leave because she got mad at me? I hoped that she didn't. I was excited to see my favorite celebrity on the train with me, but I still wanted to talk to Jolina.

Now that Ms. Felix was gone, I turned my attention and affections back to Jolina, but I couldn't see her anywhere. I turned around and looked at the opposite end of the train car, but she wasn't in sight. I then decided to walk to the next car and see if I could find her. Perhaps, she got upset and went to another car.

I ended up walking the whole length of the train, and I couldn't find her anywhere. Where was Jolina? How could she disappear like that? I walked back to my original seat, where we sat together, and sat back down. As I put my leg in the aisle, I kicked something. It was a piece of balled up paper from what looked like Jolina had torn out and balled up and forgot to throw away on the train, or must've fallen out of her bag.

I picked it up and opened it up. It said: "*Love Now, Not Later. A Song by Jolina Felix.*"

Jolina Felix? Felix was her last name? Wait, Jolina Felix? No, wait, that's a big coincidence.

"*Wait, that's not possible*" I thought. How does Jolina have the same last name as Ms. Felix?

Was that her mother? No. Jo Jo Felix doesn't have a daughter. Jolina also said she didn't know Ms. Felix, or heard of her before. It must have been a coincidence. Plus, which daughter would not sit next to their mother while traveling…

That's when it hit me.

My favorite singer's name was Jo Jo Felix. Oh, wait! Jo Jo Felix did write and perform a song called *"My Love is for Now, Not Later"* in her first album!

I don't think it's possible. It *couldn't* have been. No. How? That's impossible. Was I really talking to…?

The train jolted to a stop and announced that it arrived at my station. I opened my eyes and raised my head and looked up and saw the poem about dreams that I saw right before I drifted off to sleep. I was back in my original seat, and I was at my station. I turned my head and looked across the aisle. Jolina was not there.

I rubbed my eyes and stood up to get off the train. As I walked down the steps, I lamented at myself. This was not possible, I thought. Yet, I had met my favorite singer. It was her. Long before she was famous. Long before she became what she was now. Jolina Felix *was* Jo Jo Felix. How could I have not recognized her? How could I have not seen that it was her? I had chosen to ignore her, all for the chance to meet her future celebrity self, when the authentic, past version was sitting right next to me, and actually liked me. *Me*, of all people. She was interested in me, and I blew it.

I wanted to cry.

I was having the worst day. I had almost been ripped off and conned, and now, some kind of universal dimensional time paradox had allowed me to meet my favorite celebrity when she was younger, and I missed the chance to become close friends with her before she was famous, and who knows? Maybe we could have been even more. I missed my chance, all because I was focused on the wrong thing. But how could I have known? How could I have realized it?

As I walked towards my building, I thought about how pathetic a guy I was. I even foolishly tried to recall the numbers Jolina had told me while we sat together, having that most amazing conversation, in hopes I could call her. But of course, I couldn't remember the numbers, because they were never there.

I had missed the chance to be with Jolina.

I started to cry, but then I stopped. I had to remind myself.

Remind myself of the impossibility of what I just experienced, and the impossibility of this time paradox I found myself in. I reminded myself…

That it was all just a dream…

…I think…

Weird Request Day

"What is so uniquely weird, about the one strange thing of which you are paired? Or who, for the clean suck-able "finger" actually cared?

S o um…yeah, I can't say for certain when this day came about, or who had the bright idea to suggest this day. I just know I'm living in it.

Before I begin, I just want to say that I don't necessarily have a problem with this day, and most people just have fun with it. As for me, I am one of those types of guys that don't question When a good thing or bad thing comes their way. I'm mellow like that.

Now that you know that riveting information about me, let me tell you all about this day.

It's Weird Request Day!!!

As I sat at work watching people take full advantage of this day, I wondered how much I really could get away with myself? At this point, you're probably wondering what the hell is Weird Request Day? What are you talking about Sir? Yeah, probably should've started with that.

As it turns out, some genius Nobel prize-winning psychologist had the bright idea to suggest one day in the year where you can actually *get away* with any weird request that you had. It was meant to, frankly, stem the tide of "human foolishness". Heh. You plagiarizing son of a bitch. Nobel prize my ass.

As it stands, it doesn't matter what the request is, it could be anything. Now of course you can't go crazy. I mean you can't request to kill somebody or anything like that. It also means you can't walk around trying to sexually assault women or generally hit babies or monstrous stuff like that. You know, it has to be well within reason, and all laws are still enforceable of course, but the requests can be and do get pretty weird.

As to the level of weirdness that you tend to, or want to display is up to you, but most people use it as an opportunity to kinda fulfill the secret desires of their hearts without being necessarily looked down upon. Of course, this is just for this day.

My office colleagues acted as if this was Christmas. I saw my secretary "request" to unplug all the phones in the office. Meh. Childs play. I listened to my co-worker's request of each other a sample of their pee. That, I admit was a little freaky. But I think it was for passing a "certain" upcoming test, more so than just for freakiness. So, who knows? But yeah, all within the realm of Weird Request Day. Honestly, to me, it's like Christmas, but without the fa-la-la-la-la and more like "the hell is happening here?" type thing. See? You get the picture.

Some requests were sweet. One guy *requested* to take his crush out to dinner. Too bad though, as his crush *requested* to decline.

What? It was not funny at all! I'm just wiping my eyes since it teared up with sadness. That's all. I didn't bend down and suppress any laughter…Eh. hem.

Anyway, moving on.

Some requests were just downright sick and demented. The housekeeper requested to clean the bathroom with herbal disinfectant and environmentally-friendly cleaners, made by Clorox instead of Lysol. He said he wanted to try something new. The sick bastard. You choose Clorox over Lysol? I mean, who does that? Who cleans the bathroom with bleach? Was he trying to kill us all?

But of course, the list goes on and on.

I told myself this year, I wasn't gonna be like those simple, petty people. No. no. I was gonna be so freaky and lopsided, that people would remember my *weird request* for years. Again, I wasn't gonna request to slap a puppy or something like that, I was just gonna outdo all other requests this year.

Perhaps, lick the office door three times, then run around with my necktie tied to my left ear and jiggle my right toe while reciting America the beautiful…wait no, no. That would be too dangerous. People might like that too much. Or perhaps, I could go full-on weird freak, and mix some milk with orange juice. Yeah, I might do that. That's some sick twisted business right there. Off the rails up in this *bizniz*. Mix orange juice with milk. Yeah. That's right. You like that, huh? You like that, you sick milk-curdling bastard?

While I was at home the day before, I started thinking about it. I knew I wanted to do something, but I knew it had to be big. Tons of ideas floated through my mind. I mean, I wanted to do something so weird, I would be "WRD king" as we called it at work. The thing is, it's not so easy to do that with all these bright, wonderful, calm, imaginative people out here though. People are so grounded and sane. No one has any issues. I wish I was so grounded. People inspire me. No one ever has any issues at all. Ever. Must be sweet living like that.

But I digress. At work, I wanted a promotion. I mean, I felt like I earned it. I did a lot of work. I had a boss who had the squarest of knees. Her knees were so damn square. For the life of me, and don't tell her this, but every time she crossed her legs, I wanted to touch her knees. I just wanted to be like *"can I touch your knees?"* Nothing sexual or anything, I just wanted to touch her knees. To tell you the truth, she probably *would* let me, but I knew the request was kinda weird, so I never asked.

I never asked about a lot of things. *Why are things the way they are? Why do boogers fly when you chuck them? Why don't they just remain stuck to your finger?* I mean, aren't they sticky? *I'm right, aren't I?* Also, *how come paper cuts sting? Why is this girl sitting across from me staring at my fingers as I type?* Also, *why do we even work anyway?* I mean, can't we all just stay home and just go to the supermarket and pick up stuff for free? Food doesn't run out, right? Neither does sunlight. It's not like we have to make plants grow. They grow on their own. Humans are stupid. I mean, just think about it.

But anyway, as I was saying…

Oh, wait? so, you're interested in what I just said? About the Sun? Wait, how am I wrong? What are you talking about? Isn't there an unlimited amount of food? Come on man…Oh, you mean the line before the work thing? Oh, no, I got you. You meant the comment I made about the girl sitting across from me staring at my fingers! Oh ok yeah. Well, she kinda does that. She seems like she is obsessed with other people's fingers.

From what I heard, her mother didn't want to breastfeed her as a baby and instead shoved formula down her throat, and when she'd go for a tit, her mother wouldn't breastfeed her, and when she'd cry, her mother would substitute her finger for a pacifier, and she'd just suck and suck away.

Honestly, genius-level intellect really. All mothers should do that. Do you know how much money you can save on pacifiers? Shoots. Probably a billion dollars, easily. Boy, I could buy a lot of people some knee straighteners with that kind of money.

You still wanna talk about her? Why? She's a normal girl. Nothing special about her. She's just into fingers. That's nothing really. I even let her suck on my finger once. As I recall, it was last year's weird request day. It kinda happened by accident though. She had just heard that her grandmother's cat's buddy had passed, and she was crying at her desk. Everyone knew. She loved that cat. No, not her grandmother's cat, I said her grandmother's cat's deceased cat friend.

Listen, don't ask me. I don't know, and I don't want to know. She loved her grandmother's cat's friend who apparently lived in the dumpster at the back of her building. From what I understand, the alley cat had licked her finger once. Or was it her that licked his paw? Ah. I can't remember.

Anyways, she was crying at the side of the supplies closet, and I needed to get some paper, so I went over to quietly grab the paper and I intended to whisper to her that her grandmother's cat's best friend wasn't suffering anymore, and was happy in alley cat heaven. I bet it's a nice place too. Rotten bananas and spoilt tuna fish galore. Plus, all the rats you can find to snap their necks and kill. Then I bet since it was alley cat heaven, they don't die, *the rats*, I mean. They just come back to life and the cats get to snap their necks again. All in perfect alley cat bliss….

"Can I suck on your thumb?"

"Huh?" I asked, as this kinda caught me by surprise.

"Ok, maybe you won't let me suck on your thumb, but I'm sad, can I suck on one of your index fingers?"

I looked at the poor thing. She seemed like she needed it. And I, as a gentleman and a scholar, could not abandon this request. What type of man would I be if I said no? How could the honor of men not spring forth like a rushing wave to conquer the fires of *un-remitted finger suck*ers? No. I would rise to the challenge. I'm brave like that. I would meet the finger sucking request with no less fervency as her dead friend's ravenous rat killing sprees he so mightily displayed on many occasions while he was a part of this world.

"This is my weird request for today." She said.

I said *"Sure, let me just put down the paper I have, and I'll be right back"*

She wanted me to hurry back, as her need to suck my finger was the only thing that would help her through this crushing grief of losing her mighty cat friend. I walked away in haste, ready to come back to perform my duties. *I am a man,* you know? This was my chance to prove how much I matter. Shoots. Men don't get these chivalrous opportunities anymore.

As I turned the corner, I wondered if I should wash my hands. After all, she needed my fingers to not have the scent of paper and ink on it right? I also remember sticking my *left hand* near my crack when I felt a slight itch earlier today.

Oh, give me a break. I know what you wanna say. Don't worry, I itched the scratch over my underwear, so my finger never touched the actual skin near my butthole to scratch it. It was the underwear cloth that did it. The cloth touched my skin. I just manipulated the cloth near my crack. My index finger got close, but I made sure to rub in the cloth good and firm. I even checked my finger after I pulled it out of my underwear. Nothing on it. Only a slight smell, I think. Meh. I got used to it and I think the smell was fine. See? I avoided disaster. Plus, it was at least thirty minutes ago. See? I'm not stupid. No germs should be there.

When I got back to the closet, she was waiting there and beckoned me into the nearby room. I closed the door. I mean, you don't need an audience to see you save someone right? Heroes don't mitigate disasters for attention. They do it because they are heroes.

She asked me which finger she was allowed to suck on and I said anyone is good, but that she should pick what makes her happy. I sat and placed my hands out. Now, I have large hands, and my thumbs are pretty big. She initially reached for my thumb, but then, remembering that I may not like it, she thought better of it, and asked me if the index finger was ok.

I said sure, and I gave her my right hand. Then I pulled back. She had a small surprised look on her face. *"What's wrong?"* She asked.

You see, I had forgotten what finger I used to scratch my crack. Was it the right hand? Or the left? Wait, didn't I scratch my crack with both hands? Now I was confused! I couldn't remember. I realized time was going by and I didn't want to keep her waiting any longer, so I decided that I had scratched my crack with my right hand, since I'm right-handed, and I gave her my left hand.

Safe! Phew! I almost caused a tragedy there! She sucked my left index finger for a while then said that for some reason, it reminded her of her deceased cat friend. She said she would let him into her grandmother's house through the window, and he would go greet his friend. She said she always knew they were playing, cuz' she heard screams and hissing, and could only imagine how much fun they were having. Then, she said, every single time before he left, he would for some reason roll around in the litter box then head out. She said my finger smelled like him. She said she didn't know why, and if I had any idea or reason why.

I mean, I was just as flummoxed as her. I mean, how could I even figure that out? Meh. What do I know? Guess I just have that familiar scent. I don't know where it might have come from, but ok.

She said she just needed to suck on my finger for a few more moments and that would tie her over till later. I said sure, suck as much as you want. I'm just here to help. I didn't get any pleasure from it. I just wanted to help her. After maybe another two minutes, she was done, and she stood up and thanked me for my kindness and that I was the only one who cared enough to make sure she was ok.

See fellas? That's how it's done. You wanna do all in your power to be the type of man that lets a girl suck on his finger, even if you don't know the reason. You don't have to know the reason. Just be a man, dammit.

After that, she walked out and asked me to enjoy the rest of Weird Request Day, and that if I had a weird request, she would fulfill it. I told her maybe next year.

Fast forward to this year, and homegirl is staring at my fingers again. Nah. She's gonna have to wait. I got work to do. As I sat at my desk, my boss emailed me and asked me what their schedule looked like for the next two weeks, and if I wanted to attend a presentation that was scheduled for the next few days. My boss said we could go over it when I saw her that afternoon.

At the end of the day, I stopped by the boss's office to leave the schedule and I asked how she spent the day. My boss said it wasn't too bad, but that it wasn't as weird as she would have liked. A client had complained, so she was dealing with that issue instead.

I laughed and said mine was more normal than yours probably. Then we both chuckled and again, she crossed her legs and exposed those damned square knees.

Instantly, I had the thought, to just go for it. I mean, it *was* Weird Request Day. Maybe she would be inclined to let me touch them. Again, just the knees folks. No inappropriate business here. Not trying to go to jail for harassment. Just putting that out there.

Again, just to repeat for all you sick bastards out there, I am not attracted to my boss, I just wanted to touch those damned square knees. That's all. Seriously, I was just curious as to how they got that shape, and how come she could walk with them being so damned square.

As I was about to say it, just as I was about to utter the words, my boss said:

"*So…I have a weird request for you.*"

I looked at her and she wasn't smiling or anything. She just had this look on her face that meant it was a serious request.

"*Sure, what?*" Boy, do I regret saying that.

She continued. "*I was wondering if you'd…*"

The door slammed open as someone walked through the corridor and the office phone rang at the same time. But I heard it. I freaking heard it. My boss looked at me, then kept staring at me as she picked up the phone. It was one of our important clients. They wanted to discuss something. I was kinda in shock and froze up. I had just heard the weirdest request of my life. I just backed out of the room to give my boss and the client some privacy. My boss was beckoning me to stay, but I pretended to look at my phone and walked away.

I vomited in the bathroom down the hall. The request was the weirdest shit I have ever, ever heard. No, it wasn't nasty. No, it wasn't sexual. No, it wasn't anything harmful to myself or her. It was just weird. Present and shocking, yet simple in its *requexistence.*

Yes, it was just there. There, lingering like the concept of gravity, existing in its weirdness as no other person could have possibly thought or fathomed to conceive.

My boss had asked me to….

Wait, maybe I don't say it. It's just too weird. I don't think you could take it. If I told you how weird it was, you might faint from the weirdness. Or vomit, as I did. Even though I'm a tough chap, with a strong constitution.

As I drove home, I wondered how could someone think up such a request? Was this some sick joke?

As I lay in bed, I wondered how my boss came about this request. Maybe I should tell you. I don't know. You decide for yourself.

You see, my boss had asked me to...no wait...nevermind.

The Bad Advice

"What lieth within the heart of the beauty keep, a spoilt treasure to find, for it is not very deep; True beauty may be found, below the gleaming white surface, but to the root, you must dig, you must dig deep on purpose."

O *h boy! It's already so warm today! I can't wait until the sun comes up! I think I better wake up early and stretch. While I'm at it, let me just drink some water. Gotta keep hydrated"*

The weather was predicted to get pretty warm today. Our girl, the main character of this story, didn't look at any temperature gauge to know that though. She was able to easily feel it. She already knew it.

"Can't wait for the Sun today! I can already tell, it's gonna be a nice day today. I think I'm ready. I think I need to exercise too."

She knew the importance of exercise, and so she regularly performed physical activity to stay healthy and fit.

"Ok, so one-two, and stretch. One-two and stretch again! Ah. That feels better. Sometimes I'm stiff. It's not easy to move sometimes. But it matters not, because I'm beautiful baby!"

She was a little vain. No, scratch that. She was *very vain*. All of the females in her group were. After all, they *were* gorgeous. Not too bright or knowledgeable, but gorgeous. They were all quite young after all.

"I'm thirsty. I better drink a little more water and keep hydrated."

Nothing wrong with that. It was gonna be hot. Gotta keep hydrated.

"Do you think he'll stop by again today? I'm telling all you ladies right now; he likes me the best. And I'm kinda in love with him. So honestly, some of you should just give up. No, really."

The competition was fierce. She was competing for his attention along with some of the other ladies who lived nearby. It was indeed fierce because as I said, they were *all* gorgeous.

"*Why do you think you deserve him? Get out of here. I have just as much right!*"

They constantly argued amongst themselves. Over this one single guy. He made it a point to stop by almost every day, and when he did, they went out of their way to *seduce* him.

"*Ladies, don't quarrel. I'm older than all of you, and even I know he can't be with all of us. I mean, look at me. I'm mature, but still, I look amazing. Maybe he will want to get with me.*"

Unlike what we normally see, where young girls are seen as more attractive than older women, for they shine with the beauty of youth; in this circumstance, it was the solid opposite. The oldest woman was very attractive. Immensely more attractive than the younger girls. There was another guy who was interested in a younger girl, but as soon as he saw the older female, he was smitten. They ended up getting together and she had a few kids.

"*Of course, you always get the men. Just because you are slightly taller and more beautiful. Well, not today. Besides,*" *you know you already have a family, why on earth would you try to get with another guy?"*

Being she was the most attractive, she had developed a reputation of being the most promiscuous, when in fact, men took one look and wanted to do everything they could to get at her. This wasn't *entirely* her fault.

"Because I can. And so? As long as none of you ladies don't run your mouth, why can't we all enjoy?"

Now that I think about it, that was the wisest thing a female in her position could say.

"Just stop. I'm gonna get me that guy today. I'm telling you right now. I plan on wearing my best perfume. I will be irresistible, bitches."

She sure wasn't gonna let the older chick steal her man today. The competition was getting fierce. You know women stop playing when they start calling each other "bitches".

"Listen, ladies, it's gonna be very hot today. Make sure you drink a lot of water and be ready because business will be booming. We may even see more than one guy. I advise you all to wear your best perfume if you wanna attract that hot guy."

Such was their womanly commotions and ramblings. When our girl, the main female looked around, she knew that they were all gorgeous. She didn't feel right. She knew perhaps one of those other ho's will be looking to take the one guy she was eyeing up. She looked at herself. She was cute, but she knew she needed work. At least, in comparison to the mature older lady. So, against her pride, she went to seek her advice. She would beg for help from the most attractive woman there.

"Can you please help me? I really want him. I think we can both be truly happy, but I fear someone may take him from me. There's just so many of us."

Now, I wanna point out, that the men that came by, they weren't really what you call *monogamous*. But you couldn't stop a young girl in love.

"Ok, my dear. I will help you. After all, we are all in this thing together. The first thing you want to do is slump your shoulders and bow your head."

This was poor, self-defeating advice. You see, while I mentioned that the older lady was indeed the most beautiful, she was also the most jealous and the most devious.

"Are you sure? I guess so. If you say so."

Our young girl was very trusting and optimistic, and while she was surely not the smartest lady there, she was becoming to be very attractive herself, almost starting to rival the older woman.

"Also, don't wear as much perfume. You can wear a little bit, but you wanna be subtle. You don't wanna blast him with all that scent you know? He will be turned off."

The older lady sure was sneaky. All the other females would be wearing very nice perfume and plenty of it. This piece of advice would make the men in fact, avoid her, and go to the other women. Man, I tell you. This older chick was spiteful.

"Really? Ok. I will do that."

So very trusting, our girl. *Too* trusting.

"Lastly, whenever he comes near you, you wanna ignore him a little. He may come very close to you, he might even wanna make eye contact with you, but don't look at him. Keep your head down."

This was so wrong. I stopped liking the older chick after that.

"Ok, I trust you. I will do that."

After our young girl left, an hour or two passed, and then, as they had all hoped, he came by.

"Oh look at me! Look at me, cutie! Look at me handsome!"

They all shouted at him. All except for our young girl. But it didn't matter, because he didn't notice any one of them. There was simply no chance. He too, was smitten by the older woman. She was just too attractive. Contrary to the horrible advice she had given our girl, *she* had her shoulders perked up. *She* had her face all freshly washed and makeup was done beautifully. She even maintained perfect eye contact. Her body looking amazing, but her face was especially cute. There was no chance. He went straight to her.

"Why? Every single damn time! This is not fair"

The ladies all looked on and spoke quietly amongst themselves as they saw that the man only wanted the more mature lady. Our girl had trustingly followed the advice of the older woman, and she did not see that the guy she wanted so badly went right past her. She stayed that way almost all day, with a slumped shoulder, head facing down, looking at no one, hoping he would see her.

The man had spent what appeared to be a good hour or so fornicating with the older lady when suddenly, there was a dark cloud that overshadowed the sky. One of the ladies started to scream. They were looking at the mature lady to ask what they should do.

"Oh no, someone's pulling me hard! Oh God! It hurts! It hurts!"

Someone had thus attacked the older, more mature woman. She was screaming so hard, but it seemed to do nothing. In one instant, she was pulled by her legs, then cut in half.

She died instantly.

Why would anyone do this? What was the meaning behind such a cruel thing?

For you see, a small child had come by the garden, and she, as all humans have come to do when they see a gorgeous, mature, sweet-smelling *sunflower*.

They *pluck* it.

Animals Unite

"At last we reach the final tale, of human and beast interaction, will there be a chance to avenge the dog's untimely death, enough for animal satisfaction?"

For what seemed like the last few days, Animals marched in large groups, heading in the direction of the center of all major cities and governments, gathering in convenient pockets close to parks, forests woodlands and other areas where they could be comfortable, yet close enough to humans to congregate when necessary.

Police barricades and roads were blocked to accommodate the long processions of various groups of animals, with many wildlife conservatory people leading the way to avoid the destruction of property by wild beast and to protect against malicious acts of violence against any animals as they congregated.

Many animals, despite their wild natures, stood and walked intelligently amongst people, within their confines, refraining from attacking man or prey unless necessary for sustenance. Massive amounts of food and feed were provided by sympathetic humans for the animals that chose to stay within the limits of cities and human dwellings. Not all animals could come or fit within human confines, and these larger animals, especially those whom people could not tolerate so close to civilization, were allowed to gather just outside city limits and close by environments.

As the animals gathered, many conversed amongst themselves in small groups, planning and deciding what must be done, and how they should go about defending themselves if the humans should attack. Many feared that the humans would thus continue to be unreasonable, but thanked the good humans, who along with most of the people cheering them on, had their best interest at heart.

Many humans, now able to interact with animals and species never before seen up close and free, sought personal interaction and interviews with them. These requests were accepted with delight by many of the animals, for they wanted to tell their side of things, and happily submitted to all requests from newscasters and broadcasting channels, seeking access to them.

One such interview between an Owl and a young reporter stood out among the many:

"Hi, I'm Jennifer Thomas of the Channel 3 evening news. How should I address you? Would you like to be called by any specific name?" She asked, nervously.

"Well, you can just call me Mr. Spots if that is easier for you."

He was a North American Spotted Owl.

"Ok, that works. Thank You. So Mr. Spots, can you shed some light on what is happening here? Why are all the animals congregating?"

"Firstly, thank you sincerely, my dear Ms. Thomas, for allowing me a chance to expound upon the purposes of our compunctual presentations. We are here, not to invade or to start a war, but to seek answers as the egregious crime that has been committed against the trust and faith of all animals.

We seek an explanation of the reason as to why the Dog, our spokesperson and representative, was thus brutally murdered, and to what extent justice will be administered, as this is a crime not against one animal, but substantially magnified even more so, as a crime perpetrated against the entirety of the animal kingdom."

"I appreciate that response, Mr. Spots. From our latest reports, it appears that the police are still looking for clues and evidence as to who might have committed this horrific crime, and the investigation appears to be ongoing."

"I realize indeed, the quite immense task of locating a person or persons who could have committed this dubious act, but my kind, along with the entire animal kingdom urge all of human-kind to see our case, and understand our marked frustration and ethereal disturbance at such atrocities shown to us, as we exemplified nothing but patience and peace-loving practicalities to the human race, since obtaining our ability to fundamentally converse with you."

"I know that you might not have a clue as to who might have done this, but can you tell me if there was anything unusual or strange that was happening around the Dog before this senseless murder? Did he perhaps, receive any threats of violence towards himself or any other animals?"

The Owl looked at the reporter for a second, closed his eyes, then opened them again.

"My dear Ms. Thomas, we are animals. Do we not constantly fear for our lives from prejudiced human attacks and biased treatment? When has the human not threatened our lives and submitted towards us, proclamations of harm and death? No, it has always been thus. As for this terrible matter, we only have small suspicions, and we do not yet have iron-clad details on the circumstances, but I assure you, we have our satisfactory methods of investigation, and we have already appointed a specialized team of expert trackers and scent identifiers, to sort this matter out thoroughly, and identify the perpetrators at guilt."

"So what you're saying, is that animals are investigating? Are you telling me that animals are conducting their independent investigations within separate groups?" The reporter asked excitedly.

"Why yes, certainly, Ms. Thomas. We can see clearly and cleanly at night. We can pick up scents that humans do not know are even present. The one mistake our culprit did not take into consideration, is that humans commit crimes as humans, but as you undoubtedly know Ms. Thomas, we are

not human. We will identify and bring to light this evil being, and we will then turn over our findings to appropriate law enforcement, according to the resolution that was to be signed before this disturbing incident."

"That is very interesting to hear, Mr. Spots. Do animals intend to work alongside human investigators to shed light on this crime together?"

"Well, we are open to it, as we want to bring this matter to as speedy a conclusion as possible. We hope to find the progenitors of this crime as quickly as possible, but if humans request our assistance, we shall provide it. We fully intend as the animal kingdom had agreed to do, to abide by the precedents of the Human-Animal Resolution. I pray that Humans continue to work with us as well, and uphold their end of our joint accord."

"I truly hope so too, Mr. Spots. Well, that's all for now. Thank you very much for providing us with your insight into this whole matter, and thank you very much for your time."

"Certainly. Anytime, Ms. Thomas. Whohoohoo whoo!"

Mr. Spots then flew away into the night.

"Well, there you have it. The animals continue to gather and are independently investigating, as they are seeking answers to this terrible crime. We will be actively watching and monitoring the situation as it develops. I'm Jennifer Thomas, reporting live in the park at night, here in Cedar Heights. Grace, back to you."

The interview was broadcast all over the world, with many animals and humans alike, watching on.

After viewing the interview, the local authorities put in requests from the animals to assist with the investigation. As days passed, people watched, as man and beast walked together, checking out clues and alerting one another to potential witnesses amongst human and beast.

Shortly after a week of investigation, with the help of the immense animal effort, the perpetrators of the crime were finally identified. It was a sole man, in his late 50's who had lost a limb to a shark attack many years ago, and hated all animals, especially large predators, and sought revenge on animals ever since then. He was implicated years back in a conspiracy to murder large groups of animals by planning to sneak into the local zoo and attempt to use poison to kill as many animals as possible. However, he was never charged, as there was not enough evidence to convict him for planning an attack he never went through with. Further, as this was not an attack on humans, and seeing as the man was handicapped, investigators decided to release him on his own recognizance.

Now found and in custody, investigators questioned and interrogated the man as to his motives and purpose for killing the Dog. The man said he almost didn't go through with it, but did it as revenge against all animals, as he watched the broadcast of the general assembly and saw that the Dog had made it known that animals know what they are doing when they harm humans. He said he despises all animals, but he wasn't going to go through with it until he heard what the dog had said.

The authorities asked him if he understood why the dog said what he said, and inquired if he realized it was part of an apology to all humans and with it, came a vow that animals would not seek to harm humans again, except if they had to defend themselves, which they understood was a real possibility.

The man answered that he knew that, but he didn't care. He said that was fine *now*, but it wouldn't bring back his leg.

Investigators then asked the man to recount what he did, and how he went about his deed, as if he told them everything, they would count it towards his bid for leniency.

The man recounted his steps. He had gotten past several blockades, as he had a crutch, and security felt he wasn't a threat to anyone. He said he used this as an advantage. He said he then lurked in the nearby park until the dark, then secretly snuck into the place where the dog was staying, and as he slept, he tied a rope around the dog's neck and began to strangle him.

The man recounted that as the dog woke up, he immediately went to bite his hand, but instead, moved his mouth away from his hand, and instead looked up at the man, providing no resistance. The man said he released the rope, allowing the dog to gasp for air, then the Dog asked him why he was attacking him. The man said, that's when he looked at the dog, pleading for his life, instead of fighting back, that it somehow threw him into a rage and he took out his small hidden pocket knife and began to stab the dog several times. Then when the dog could no longer move from his injuries, he put the rope around the dog's neck, and strangled it again, cruelly killing it.

The man, upon recounting his cruelty, began to cry.

He asked for leniency and asked that he be forgiven because an animal had cruelly taken his leg and almost his life from him, but that shark had gotten away, and so it was unfair for him to be punished.

Upon hearing this sad, horrific news of the way the Dog was killed, many animals mourned and cried, asking why the humans were so cruel. Many species began to be angry and called for the proper justice of death for the man, who had slain the first Chief Animal Representative.

Higher up governmental officials were sent in small delegations to various animal installations, providing any info they asked for, and assuring them that the man was held securely in a private cell and that he would be charged and tried appropriately.

Unfortunately, this was not to happen, for the animals would not wait for the humans to provide them justice. They would take it. Take it, as the laws of the animal kingdom demanded; swift, clean, simple justice.

The next day, the authorities were shocked to find the man, choked and stung to death by deadly African Killer Bees. Some lingered in his cell as proof that it was done by animals, and not by coincidence.

The bees turned themselves in.

One bee stated that it was simple to wait till the man opened his mouth to snore, and one of their comrades flew into his throat, and lodged himself there, stinging him and causing his throat to swell instantly, and sacrificing himself for the rest. The rest then silently flew into his cell two to three at a time and begun to sting him as he struggled and gasped for air. When they realized he was also allergic, they knew their task would be that much easier and continued to sting him until he was dead.

As the authorities looked at the surveillance tape, they discovered it was just as the bees had said. The man was killed, mercilessly by the bees, sent as harbingers of death, by the animal kingdom for justice for his cruel crime.

Upon discovery by the public to what had taken place, many people cheered on the animal kingdom's justice and called for the matter to end and for things to move on, now that the man had died. They reasoned that it was unfortunate, but weighed the man's life as equal to the crime he insidiously committed, in murdering the Dog, so brutally and mercilessly.

Many, however, did not thus feel so equivalently. Many argued that animals had no right to exact justice upon humans and that he should have been tried in human courts, not secretly sentenced to death by vengeful animals. Many held the sentiment that if allowed to continue, animals would seek to exact revenge for the slightest trespasses or visit upon man payback for the more egregious of human sins against them. After all, what was to stop them? If they could fly in and sting the life out of a person, what would stop those tiny assassinating bastards from murdering presidents and very important personnel while they slept?

A divide was now beginning to emerge. Many people, once sympathetic to animals, began to now treat them with disdain. Many enraged people began to attack and kill the weaker and lesser species, as they peacefully cohabitated within human dwellings. Police were being called to various areas, as it would be initially quiet, but then the sound of a screeching animal could be heard in the night, as it was beaten and murdered in revenge by unforgiving and zealous humans.

This began happening all over the world, as people, no longer respectful of the accord, began to treat animals as the enemy.

As animals complained of the prejudice and violence they faced, the security council convened and issued a statement that asked all animals to withdraw from human dwellings and to retreat to their living areas as before. Many animals left, but some animals refused to leave. They said they wanted to stay to work things out with the human, and requested that the violence against them to stop, or they would be forced to defend themselves.

A mother bear, enraged and heartbroken upon finding one of her cubs slaughtered by a group of men, threatened to take revenge on the men, and proclaimed to a nearby camera as she wept, that animals would declare *war* on the humans.

This statement, although said by a mother bear who, just as a human, can be forgiven for a temporary loss of decorum, especially after finding a brutally murdered child, was upheld by anti-animal groups, who stated that this was the true intention of the animals and that they really wanted war with all humans, so they could eventually take over, and that if it was a war they wanted, they would get it.

In reality, it was zealous, trigger-happy humans, who itching for the chance to use their weapons against animals, wanted to incite a war to kill animals freely, just as they always did previously under the guise of "hunting and culling".

Disturbed by the potential for war amongst animal and beast, The UN sent envoys to the most intelligent species of animals, along with letters of democratic proclamations that humans did not desire war with animals. The animal councils replied in earnest, imploring humanity to cease their senseless killing of animals out of hatred, and for the accord to be completed, signed and adhered to.

Many animals began to feel as if the snake, despite his jealousy and hate, was *right*.

They felt that perhaps it was a curse, rather than a blessing that they were allowed to speak and converse with the human, for the human will find some way, to corrupt and destroy any good thing, and despite the humans who did good by them, they were suffering even more from cruelty and mistreatment. Some animals began to regret wanting to work alongside the human to make the world better.

The animals held another vote worldwide, and this time, they appointed the Great Gorilla to be the *Chief Animal Representative*. He would travel with a small escort always, despite his size and strength, and negotiate matters going forward. This was enough to appease the remaining animals who stayed, and many returned to their natural habitats.

In a secret meeting behind closed doors amongst several presidents and their personal security, the Great Gorilla and his detail of animals discussed and debated how best to deal with the whole matter.

The Great Gorilla further expounded on the ideals of the animal kingdom as set forth by the Dog previously. He sought to show the leaders of the human world that even though things were going the way they were, animals still yet held no lasting ill-will and only sought to make peace, once and for all with humans, and make the world a better place.

Said the Gorilla:

"Despite everything that has happened, let us come together. There is no need for this senseless violence."

"We want the same thing, my friend. But remember, it is animals who could not wait for justice. We would have sentenced him to many years in prison." Said one of the leaders.

"I deeply apologize on behalf of all animals, for this was not the way justice should have been served. However, surely you can understand our immense frustration at the blatant hatred shown thus to animals, who seek only a peaceful, helpful accord with humans."

"I understand, but animals simply cannot go around enacting their own justice."

"I understand this sincerely my human brothers and sisters. As such, it will now be outlawed for any animal to

ever commit such a crime again against man. *No animal, once bound by a promise before the creator would then dare break such an oath.*"

"Ok, fair enough. Now tell us what animals want. We have no intention to stop drilling for oil. Not right now, at least."

"*For now, my human friends, we only seek peace, and the institution of the accord, as feasible to humans as possible. We can then establish a semi-annual conference, where we may meet to further provide insight into these affairs. For now, the resolution would be enough, and signal to all that we have finally codified the agreement, and that animals and man will jointly work together to better the planet and not harm each other.*"

"And again, what about any animal that causes harm to humans? Should we take this as a betrayal of our trust? What will you do in response to this?"

"*I assure you, my trusted friends, no animal will break their oath, once taken. This is the law of all animals that we all abide by. Since the beginning of time. We will not break it, as long as humans keep their word to us.*"

"We can't be responsible for random outliers. In other words, we can't be responsible if someone goes against the resolution. It's people. Not everyone agrees."

"We know, and as such, when we ratify the resolution into law and we take our oath, it will include waiting to see justice served upon any humans who maliciously defy the accord. We only ask that it be codified as strongly as possible, for instance, a document to be held as sacredly, if not more than the United States constitution itself. What say you?"

The President of the United States, as she was in attendance, nodded her head, and agreed to vote for the resolution with the other security council members to ratify the resolution, and for it to only be changed or amended with the consent of animals and humans alike.

Thus finally, after what seemed like a tumultuous amount of time, the Resolution *between Man and Beast* was signed and codified into international law.

Finally, animals could celebrate. Many species were seen on TV, thanking humans for their goodness and kindness, and expressed a desire to live closer to humans, permitting their acceptance.

The world began to change.

Animals, now less fearful to interact with humans, began to come and live closer to human dwellings than ever before, with larger, wilder species wandering closer to civilization, with less fear of being attacked.

The effects of this were amazing. Zoos now had less work to do, as animals cleaned up mostly after themselves. The monkeys stopped slinging their feces out of spite. Many natural wildlife parks and conservatories, opened their doors to allow animals to come in and out amongst humans, greeting them as they ventured out into the wild, then returning as they saw fit.

Animals began to only prey upon each other as necessary and did not waste kills. Instead, they attempted to share land and territory space with other animals who were like natured and killed when necessary for sustenance. Besides carrying on with normal animal life, many animals began to thus help the human when in danger, and instead of watching them die in situations they could assist, they immediately jumped in and saved many a human life.

Things were not perfect, however, for now, animals could voice their complaints, and many herbivores still cried out in complaint of being hunted for food by the other carnivores, and now, with a sympathetic understanding ear, many humans sided with these animals like never before.

Various groups were formed to address these issues and more, but it was all done, as peacefully as possible. Humans found themselves mediating more between beast and beast, instead of between human and beast.

New laws were made to help govern these issues, for animals still had to kill and eat to survive, but now, animals were allowed to only do so up to a point to sustain themselves, and nothing more. No more gratuitous killing as done previously.

Animals were happy. People, now living closer to animals were also happy.

The semi-annual conferences were planned and attended, with animals still advising and cautioning humans against the corruption and abuse of the planet's resources and admonishing wrongdoing whenever it was needed.

Many new policies were put into place that resulted in improved habitats and environments for all animals and humans alike.

And thus, the story of the animal and its new-found speech comes to an end.

I only pray for the accord to be upheld, and for all animal life to remain in harmony, as much as possible, with humans.

I pray it lasts for as long as possible, and that this story, while no longer being told here, never ends. Not as long as I, an animal *myself,* has the speech to tell it.

The Chicken's Life

*"A story of bravery and one of care, the chicken is not an
animal filled with fear. You may think as much from the
commonly used word, but this is the true yard fowl's story,
one you haven't heard."*

This story is a peculiar one, and one you *think*
you may have heard before. Surely, movies
and grand animations attempt to bring this
story to life. But this is *not* the truth of it at all. I have
witnessed, for quite some years, the true story of the
chicken. You will certainly be amazed at what you
hear, and I don't think you've quite heard it the way
I will tell it. This is the story of the chicken's life,
from start to end.

My father brought me and my brothers to my
parent's home country, where we spent a few years

of our boyhood, living and learning all about the third world, and how other people lived outside the states. These experiences shaped who I am today, and as such, I can tell you these experiences exactly as witnessed.

I will start by saying that there is a peculiar hilarity and amusement that revolves around the yard fowl as they go about their daily life. The machinations and peculiarities of these birds are quite hilarious, but also very serious and their lives expound on concepts of bravery, courage, comeuppance, and triumph. It is a story of the young, the old, the brave, the strong, the smart, and the disciplined.

Chickens are by nature, happy little things, content to go about their daily lives, as they don't require more than feed, water, and a place to scratch and graze. As such, one would not venture to think that such serious things as mentioned in the previous paragraph are inherent within the life of a yard fowl, but I assure you, all these elements do come into play. It was wonderful watching and observing these amazing birds as they lived their simple, but extremely interesting lives, and how similar their stories are to warriors, kings, and royalty if ever there was one. I attest to you, these facts are true, and I do not fabricate one single event or reasoning. I will tell this story as honestly as I experienced it, and as it happened

Let us begin.

When a hen comes of age, she is mated with, by the rooster, or as the country folks say, the *"Fowl Cock"*. I am not lying. I am fully aware of how that sounds, so instead of referring to male yard fowls as "fowl cocks", we will instead refer to the males henceforth as roosters. The rooster is the king of the yard, that is, among the fowls. He is the dominant male, one who has the right and ability to mate with all the hens of age in the yard. He did not get to his position easily, and that will come later, but for now, just know that as with most animals, the dominant male figure is the head, and as such, mates with the females of his choosing.

When the hen is fertilized, she produces a single egg. Once the hen is of egg-laying age, and the rooster has begun to mate with her, she will begin to lay eggs.

Hens lay a *single* egg, once a day.

This event is not marked silently in yard fowls. It is quite the opposite. When a young female lays her first egg, there is a big hubbub of squawking by the young hen, and she runs all over, exciting the whole yard and the Rooster himself, and he joins in, crowing and squawking in celebration. It is a sight to see. The young hen is celebrating the laying of her first egg. This is hilarious, but amazing to watch. The young hen is no longer just a young girl, she has now ascended and has now gained the ability to become a mother.

Now, this is where the cycle of life for chickens begin.

As the hen lays an egg, the farmer or owner may choose to take the eggs and keep them for himself. He/she is the human, and humans eat eggs of course. The hen will continue to lay eggs at a rate of one a day as long as she is of egg-laying age and is mating with the Rooster.

Now the farmer or owner usually has more than one hen laying eggs as well. Most times, a small farmer can have several or more egg-laying hens, producing one egg a day, for the foreseeable future. There does come a time when a hen gets too old to lay eggs and stops, and when that time comes, she is respectfully killed and used for meat. She can no longer lay eggs, and as such, she will no longer sit to hatch them as well. In any case, for now, you understand that as long as a hen is of age, and is mating, she will lay an egg, once a day.

As several eggs are being laid a day, the human may then begin to have more eggs than needed for the family to use. That is if he/she isn't selling eggs for a living. If that is the case, they will continue to use the eggs to make money.

But if you no longer require additional eggs for consumption, or you are now ready to breed more chickens to increase the number of livestock you have, you then allow the hen to lay, and continue laying eggs. Once a day, for approximately five to seven days.

It is at this time, that a hen makes a choice. She can choose to let her motherly instincts kick in, if she is ready, and begin to sit on them, or she may leave the set of eggs, and go about her daily life. This all depends on her age and maturity. And yes, I do mean mental maturity. You will see why soon.

Now, as I said, there is roughly a period, give or take between five and seven days, that a hen realizes who she wants to be, after seeing she has now laid several eggs, and they are all remaining there in her little laying box.

If she chooses to do hatch the eggs, she prepares herself. She will now become a mother.

A baby chicken takes approximately twenty-one days to hatch naturally, that is, by a mother hen sitting on her eggs. During that time, the farmer is supposed to shore up her little nest, giving her room to sit and coddle the eggs. She will spread herself out, and puff up her feathers if need be, and begin to sit, *tirelessly* on the eggs, for those twenty-one days or three weeks.

Now, I must tell you, not all hens are the same. Some are downright the best mothers I have seen. But some are irresponsible, lazy and the most immature beings you can ever run across. The true mother hen will, at expense of her own hunger and thirst, sit on those eggs, relentlessly for days on end, only occasionally getting up and going outside the pen or coup to relieve herself, drink some water, eat a little food, then come right back and sit there again.

I have observed this numerous times.

However, there are young mothers, who, when you find out how bad at being a mother hen they are, you want to *wring* their neck. I have seen some young mothers, sit for maybe three to five days, maybe seven tops, then get incessantly bored, and leave the eggs, never to come back, and sit on them again. This is the worst, for the eggs spoil and rotten out, for they had begun to get heat, enough to begin to develop, but nowhere near enough to hatch.

Along with these bad mothers, there are some irresponsible mother hens as well. I do not know where this comes from, for a mother's instinct is to protect and nurture, but these young, irresponsible, immature hens, will get fed up with the number of eggs in her nest, and begin to get rough with them, kicking and cracking some of them, and even causing a few to drop out of the little nest box where they were set to sit on. As a young boy, I have gone into the fowl pen numerous times and witnessed the fallen, broken egg on the floor, and the hen who is supposed to be sitting on the eggs, now sitting cozily next to the damn rooster, looking for favor. Those young ho's…um...hens, were no good.

But alas, there is a fix for this. My father showed us that when it was discovered that a hen was like this, and just lazy, immature, irresponsible and frankly, a danger to her eggs, he would remove her, sometimes forcefully from the box, kicking and screaming (Can you imagine, she doesn't want to sit on the eggs, but if you try to move her lazy ass, she will scream, which is *unbelievable*.) and take her eggs from her. What my father would do, was smart, for he would then take the still-warm eggs, and put them cautiously under the true, diligent mother hen.

If the immature hen had for instance, five eggs she was sitting on, he would take the five from the irresponsible hen, divide them up between the mature, diligent hens, and put one or two under each one. In one hundred percent of the cases, I stood and watched, as the mother hen looked at us, looked at the egg, then looked at us again, then proceeded to nuzzle the warm egg with her beak, fully under her feathers. She then readjusted herself and continued to sit, now with an additional egg or two under her. I have seen some spectacular mother hens hatch up to twelve, sometimes thirteen or more eggs at one time. They were *truly* amazing.

Some other mothers were ok, but you couldn't put too much responsibility on them. Those mothers would sit and hatch eggs, such as the screaming one above, but only if you gave her no more than two or three to sit on. Any more than that, and it would be too much for her, and she would begin to break and damage the excess eggs. So you had to know what types of personalities you were dealing with. Yes, you had to know your female yard fowl's mental personality traits, and adjust accordingly.

Some of the mature mother hens did not play around. They were strict. Very strict. Many times, we as little boys, when we would go into the pen to check on the fowls, we would stop by the sitting boxes to check on the mother hens, and they would peck the hell out of our hands if we played around with them too much, or if we shuffled the eggs too much. They never pecked my father though. Of course, they knew he was boss. But for us kids, meh. They weren't afraid and pecked the hell out of us.

After three weeks have passed, the eggs now begin to hatch.

Slowly at first, the chicks use their tiny beaks to peck a small hole into the egg, as they try to move around their legs to break apart the shell. As nature has it, many a baby chicken can successfully do this, and often break free and hatch. Some here or there, whether through position or how they developed, are unable to break fully free, or perhaps a piece of shell remains on them, and they become exhausted. I have not known mother hens to assist with the baby chicks hatching, but I suppose some may.

Occasionally, we would go and find a baby chick struggling to hatch, and we would provide careful assistance by either *gently* pulling off a small piece of the cracked shell, or repositioning the egg to give the chick some leverage to then break free. Some warn against this, as if you don't know what you're doing, you could injure the baby chick, but we learned well, from a lifelong farmer, and we never damaged a single struggling chick by doing this.

Once fully hatched, the baby chick is wet, but dries within a matter of a few hours. The chick then sits there, under his mother, awaiting his brothers and sisters to hatch. They are also able to walk within a few minutes or so. Usually, most chicks will hatch at close to the same time.

Once all chicks are hatched, the mother hen then begins to gently nudge them out the nest, and onto the ground. This does not hurt them, as they are very soft and pliable. Sometimes, she jumps down and encourages them to jump from the box to the ground. This is ok for them as well, for no pen or coup has major height, and usually the laying box is only a few feet off the ground at best. Once all chicks are on the ground, she leads them out of the pen, and into the yard, where they begin to follow her around.

The baby chick's life has now begun. Once they are a few days old, we usually go and catch them and examine them. It is here you will see if they are male or female. A simple way of checking the chick's gender is to look at the spot above their head. Roosters have a red sack of flesh growing right above their beaks. This is called the "comb". On a baby chick, if it is a male, the baby will have a tiny, white comb growing right above his head. If it is a female, the chick will not have this part noticeably present.

Now, the mother hen will take the chicks around, and begin to teach them how to scratch and forage for their own food in the yard. This is of course, in addition to the "chickfeed" the farmer or owner feeds them. Sometimes the chicks are isolated from the mother to feed them, but most times, the mother is fed and will eat the chick food, along with the chicks. It is here you also see the value of a good mother hen, for she will teach the chicks all they need to know to live. Once outside and foraging again, the mother constantly scratches and pecks the ground and shows the chicks what they must do. The chicks, instinctively mimic the mother hen and watch her as she performs her functions.

The chicks get stronger each day and can run faster, and as the days and weeks pass, they begin to grow small, tiny feathers, and shed the light-yellow fur they were born with.

* * * * *

As the chicks begin to grow, the Rooster, may embrace or ignore the chicks. Oftentimes, he ignores them and continues to keep his role as head male and defend his group. The chicks continue following around their mother and continue to grow and learn. The mother will even defend the chicks against other spiteful hens who, upon seeing them, may peck and occasionally kick them. Do they do this out of jealousy? That I do not know. All I know is that the good mother hen will do everything in her power to protect the chicks. The diligent mother hens do an amazing job of this. The rooster will do his job and fend off young upstart male roosters, who lack experience and strength, or if they become old enough to want to mate with the young hens, he actively ensures they don't get the chance. This is his struggle. He will fight until he loses this battle.

Sometimes, the dominant rooster will actively try to mate with a mother hen whilst she is walking with her chicks and it is then, that hilarity and nonsense ensues. For despite his great strength and imposing nature, he will lose this fight every time. She will turn around and peck the living daylights out of him. It is a mother's instinct; any other time in her life she will run away or give in, but not now. Now she lets him know quite sternly that she isn't playing that game, and will fight a full-grown rooster to leave her alone. The rooster tries to overpower her, but it matters not. She will peck and puff up at him until he leaves her alone. We always watched as the big bad rooster, the king of the yard, was forced to run away from a mature mother hen every time he attempted such folly.

He would then stop, and look at her, looking back and forth, wondering how in the *world* did this female hen stand up to him and make him back down. It was extremely funny to watch.

At times, it was not always funny, but serious and dangerous. Being it was an open yard, you had predators who loved to feed on one thing, and one thing only; the baby chick. After all, easy prey and soft, tender meat were up for grabs. Why not?

In the tropical countries, you had a large reptilian lizard, or what the country folks call a Salipenter, or Tegu, that thrives in the environment. They usually make their nests close by to civilization, so they can easily sneak into the yard and steal away young chicks to eat. They were *vicious* little reptiles. Think of them as a small version of the Komodo dragon. They love to sneak into the chicken coup at night and steal baby chicks or young chicks if they are small enough. However, their favorite snack is baby chicks.

One time, a Salipenter managed to sneak in. My father had a shotgun that he kept to shoot large predators when they came into the yard, and he would often use it to kill large Anaconda and

Salipenters as they tried to kill the livestock. One day, we were sitting in the house when we began to hear a commotion. You see, fowls will start clucking and squawking loudly to alert humans that something is wrong, or if they're in danger. We learned to recognize the difference between the usual nonsense squawking of an egg-laying celebration, and the alarm of real danger. This was important because when we heard the fowls cry out this way, it was often because trouble and danger were afoot. This also proved useful for us humans, as many times, they were usually the first to forage and discover the presence of a large Caiman or Anaconda, hiding in the grass, and alert the humans nearby. Many a human has been protected by the simple yard fowl.

As we ran outside to see the source of the trouble, we witnessed a brave, courageous mother hen, doing the most amazing thing. She was battling a fully grown, large Salipenter, who had snatched one of the chicks in his mouth and was attempting to run away.

I witnessed bravery that day like no other. That mother hen ran and pecked and attacked that Salipenter like the devil himself. She was not letting him go. My father called out to one of us to go run and bring the shotgun.

As we ran to get the shotgun and bullets, my father ran out towards the Salipenter, who was cut off by the fence with the baby chick still in his mouth, trying to intimidate the mother hen. But that day, he simply did not know who he was messing with. That mother hen fought like crazy and didn't let up, even when my father was running towards them and screaming at the reptile, trying to scare the Salipenter enough to drop the chicken.

Once my father got close enough to the lizard, he dropped the baby chick, which ran towards the mother and both mother and chick fled away as fast as they could. The Salipenter then took off, running away as fast as he could in the opposite direction.

I had gotten back to my father in the yard with the gun, and he immediately loaded a shot and aimed for the fleeing lizard. He didn't shoot right away. He aimed and waited for it to slow down. Once the stupid lizard stopped to make sure no one was following him, my father let off a *single* shot.

The ammunition he used was what was known as the scattershot. In other words, the Salipenter didn't have a chance. He would be killed from a multitude of lead pellets, heading his way at the speed of sound.

Before he even heard the explosion, he was dead.

I still remember to this day, the bravery and strength of that mother hen. That mother was a true fighter. It didn't matter who or what it was, short of a human themself, she was fighting it to save her chicks. Although scared for her life, it mattered not. She would fight tooth and nail to free her baby from harm. This was something we all respected.

Such was the bravery of some mother hens.

This bravery was doubly commended as well, for not all mothers ventured to do this. Some would choose, painfully so, to abandon their baby chick once captured by a lizard or snake. She had other chicks to protect and weighed it not worth it to sacrifice herself, and the lives of the other chicks to fight it. Instead, she would choose to get the rest of the chicks to safety and alert the humans to the danger. This too, is noble, for no hen can be blamed or looked down upon for trying to save their life and the lives of their babies. Real danger was present, and as long as she didn't run away, leaving *all* of the chicks to danger, she was considered a good mother. I have sadly witnessed some mothers do this as well. It is sad, but it does happen. Those mothers who did this were never allowed to sit on eggs to hatch chicks again, even if they were good chick hatching mothers.

As the chicks grow, they become teenagers and begin to go off, scratching and foraging on their own. They would forage all day and then in the afternoon, come back home to the pen and roost with all the other chickens.

For the teenager hens, they would go off, pecking and exploring their world. They continued to watch their mother, but from a distance, and oftentimes, go off with other young ladies their age, as they explore the yard and all the treasures within. They would scratch, search, peck, and dig. They would also learn to defend themselves, and learn to avoid any danger, should it present themselves in the course of their grazing.

As they become young ladies, they start to become courted by young males and the dominant rooster himself. Often, they are too young to mate, and they usually just run away from the big, imposing rooster, as they do not yet understand that he is looking to mate with them.

As for the young males; well, this is where I will leave this story off, for the males have a story unto their *own*.

The Chicken's Life II

"A story of warriors and kings, the plot will grow and thicken, this is the final part of the tale, of the indomitable chicken."

As young males begin to get bigger and stronger, their male competitive instincts begin to kick in. They often challenge each other for dominance and fight amongst themselves. They, however, stay back and watch, as the king of the yard asserts his dominance over all the hens, and watches as he is the only one who has the sole privilege of getting up at midnight and 4 am to crow. If a young rooster does this, he may be allowed to crow, but he will soon get *"cucked"* or dominated during the day by the dominant rooster.

Now for this story, I will tell it to you in the eyes of one young rooster, whom my mother loved, and named. His name was Tito.

Tito would have the most victorious and triumphant story ever told amongst chickens and yard fowl alike.

To begin Tito's story, we will go back to when little Tito was hatched.

Tito was a small chick. He had difficulty hatching and was one of those hatchlings, who my mother, upon going into the pen one day, helped hatch him by gently removing a large part of his shell, as he had become exhausted from trying to break his shell on his own.

In the yard, my father had a ritual, where he would gather all the little hatchlings a few days after they were born and walking around, and present them to my mother, to her great pleasure, as she watched, picked up and touched each little one. It became a whole thing in the family. After every hatching, my mother would ask my father when he was going to present the hatchlings to her. Even we, as boys began to look forward to it as well, knowing how amused and happy she would be to touch and bless the little hatchlings, despite being in the yard and able to pick up a little chick whenever we wanted to.

One day, as that batch of hatchlings was presented, she saw amongst them, the baby rooster, whom she had helped to hatch. The baby was special. He had short yellow fur like the rest of the chicks, but he also had a dark spot on each side of his tiny wings. He was seen to be a rooster almost immediately, and my father counted him amongst the young baby males. For that set of hatchlings, there were about three or four other young baby roosters who were hatched.

My mother instantly recognized the little chick and asked to have him brought to her, I remember picking him up and bringing him over to her. She took his little body and examined it and noticed the two little black dots on his arms. She said he would be her favorite and that she would name him. She said he was her little Tito. So that was the name she gave him.

Tito was a little spirited rooster. He had shed all his yellow fur to reveal a perfectly all over white feathered coat, with small black spots on his back and arms. He looked unlike any other fowl in the whole group. As he grew into a teenager, he was bold and very inquisitive. It was almost as if he questioned the natural way of things in the yard. "Why must *that* rooster be the head?" He must have thought. Surely, he should also be allowed to mate with these fine young women walking all over the place.

One day, when he saw that the King Rooster wasn't around, he took his chance. He was still very young, and not mature enough at all to properly do anything, but his urges were there. He would mate, come hell or high water.

As he approached one of the young ladies, he cautiously looked around and checked to make sure that the King Rooster wasn't in sight, and he then made his move. He attempted to jump on top of the young hen, who upon feeling the weight of an eager male trying to get on top of her, screamed out bloody murder. This must have been a special call or something, because I witnessed the dominant rooster appear, almost out of nowhere, and like a speeding bullet, headed straight to Tito.

Now Tito, being busy with all this hen mounting business, did not see the dominant male running towards him. No, he was too damn taken up with getting his fun, no matter the cost.

The dominant rooster had no mercy. He spurred Tito with maximum force, knocking him over, and injuring his left wing in the process. He also scratched a small part of his face.

* * * * *

When two Roosters fight, it seems gawkish and somewhat funny to humans, but I assure you, it is not. Serious blades and fangs are being flung around, capable of scratching, or blinding and incapacitating your opponent. The wings are flapped incessantly and fiercely, to try to get a "leg up" or foot up so to speak, on your opponent. The two brawling roosters relentlessly face each other, and spear each other until one either gives up, is too exhausted to fight anymore and flees, or is overpowered by the more dominant male.

What happened to young Tito, was neither that nor any of this. There was no fight. There was no challenge. Tito was defeated instantly, like a car running over a squirrel. There is no "challenge" or fight there.

Only death.

Luckily for Tito, he did not die. He was badly injured, but he lived. My mother, when she learned of this, was extremely upset, and began to beat and chase the dominant male around the yard from time to time whenever she saw him. But this was not the dominant male's fault. Must he not protect what is his? Must he not fend off invading challenges to his throne? He was king; and a king must be willing to mercilessly defend what is his. This is naturally what the dominant male did.

Tito was injured. As he retreated in pain, he ran away, far to the back of the yard to attempt to save himself. Not only was Tito injured physically, but psychologically, Tito had been destroyed. He knew he could not begin to mess around, approach, or dare challenge the dominant rooster, unless on pain of death. At the time, all the other young roosters had begun to come of age and were beginning to crow, not as strong as the dominant male, but they were crowing nonetheless.

Tito could not crow. We wondered if it was psychological damage, or if the circumstances of his life had put him at a disadvantage compared to the other young roosters. When all the young roosters would stop and arch their teenage heads and crow in the fashion of their youth, Tito would stand and watch them, but never crow.

Time had passed, and Tito's injuries began to get better. His scratch healed and almost didn't show on his face. His wing got better, and he could flap them much better than before. As he grew, he suddenly began to attempt to crow. This was somewhat late compared to the other young males, but we were glad he wanted to try now.

At first, his crow was deformed and sounded like a sick child trying to sing with a sore throat. It was bad. Poor Tito. My mother would sit at the door and encourage him to crow. "Come, Tito, don't be afraid. You can crow. I won't let the rooster get you." It seemed as if he understood her because he would then try to arch his neck and crow once more, sounding just as horrible as the last time he attempted it. We were sad to see that Tito was almost like the lowest of the low amongst the other young roosters, and often felt sorry for him. My mother, however, never gave up on him.

Tito was her child. Remember, a good mother hen doesn't *give up* on her baby chick.

Time passed. Tito took many a beating by not only the young roosters, who now felt dominant enough to fight and pick on him, but not dominant enough to challenge the King Rooster. He often took a beating even from young female hens, who for some reason just didn't respect the poor sap. Such was his time in the yard. My mother would go out and feed him and talk to him personally and keep encouraging him, despite his troubles.

Tito continued to grow. One day, things changed.

Tito was eyeing up one of the females, but older and wiser now, he knew to always keep an eye out to make sure the dominant rooster wasn't in the vicinity. Even if he wasn't, he didn't take any chances. Tito learned to attempt to mate with lighting speed. By the time the young hen cried out, he was almost done finishing up his business. That guy wasn't messing around. Sometimes he was successful, and other times, he spotted the dominant male running towards him and fled.

That day, however, Tito didn't run. I assure you; this is all true. I do not know what changed or sparked in him. Perhaps my mother's encouragement had changed him, or perhaps it was the natural order of things, and it was time for things to change. Either way, Tito did not run. Instead, he jumped back, squared up his neck, and stood ready to face down and challenge, the enraged, dominant male.

Tito did not last long. He was vanquished by the dominant male, but this time, Tito had put up a fight. He had gotten a few licks in, and Tito, for the first time, experienced a proper battle with the dominant male. This changed him.

Even though he lost to the King Rooster, Tito had become stronger. After the fight, Tito tried to crow. Despite his loss, he still crowed. It was not the strongest crow, but the crow had become better. It was a crow of defiance, a crow to signal that things were slowly changing and that his time would soon come. After all, no one lives forever. The dominant rooster could not be king *forever.*

Tito, now changed, began to take on his brothers. The young hens no longer picked on him, and instead, walked past him, and left him alone. He fought with his brothers, some battles even winning after a while, and some still losing, but nonetheless, he fought.

Tito was getting stronger every day. He began to figure out how to win battles. I know this may sound crazy, but he would wait till one of the other young roosters would try to secretly mate with a young hen, and he would use this time to attack the young rooster, while his guard was down. This method worked brilliantly, much to the amusement of my mother, who kept cheering him on to plant the smackdown on each of his brothers.

This was so funny and amusing for her. We would watch, as Tito spent many days, stalking, planning, and targeting his enemies; attacking, fleeing, and learning their weaknesses until one day, he was experienced enough to challenge them. Now armed with how they would react and how they jumped and moved, he fought them with all he had. And guess what?

He would win.

He carried out this strategy with every single one of his brothers, and each time, no matter how long it took, he came out victorious. His brothers would get beaten and flee, now forever afraid and bowing to Tito as more dominant. This was a sight to see. Every day that passed, Tito got wiser and stronger. The whole family was amused by this, for Tito was climbing the ranks, and was soon becoming a problem, even for the dominant rooster himself. This was confirmed, when one day, Tito stood up in the chicken pen, in front of all the other fowls and crowed. Still not as strong as the dominant male, but now, he had earned his place as the second strongest male in the yard, and as such, his crow was that much stronger and that much better. Tito was fast becoming a formidable rooster to be reckoned with.

* * * * *

The dominant male was not pleased. He began to look and search out for Tito, and attack him whenever he saw him. To him, he must have thought, *"Aye, isn't this the little fledgling that dared insult me some months ago? Didn't I take care of him?"* But while the dominant rooster was thinking this, Tito was also gaining fast, the confidence of the other hens in the yard. Tito had even ventured to mate with his mom, now grown, as she was still a viable female, and chickens do not have concepts of incest or such things. The thing was, she let him, and neither did she scream out. This was signaling that the females accepted him as a viable mating partner.

As Tito continued to get stronger, he would occasionally flee from the dominant male, but oftentimes, he stood his ground and fought back. Most times he lost of course, but Tito was learning. He was learning the dominant male's weaknesses and strengths. He too was gaining experience in battle, more and more, as he stepped up to challenge this dominant king.

At first, Tito would suffer quick defeats. Now, Tito was beginning to hold his own, often battling longer and fiercer each time. We always cheered on Tito, but the truth of the matter is, the dominant rooster was getting older, whereas Tito was just coming into his prime. Soon, and very soon indeed, the final battle would come. The whole family knew it was coming, and we anxiously watched and waited to see what would happen.

Finally, the fateful day came. Tito had wanted to mate with a young hen, and the dominant rooster was seemingly not having any of that nonsense on that day. For some reason, Tito was mad and fired up. So was the dominant rooster. They began to square up, and one of my brothers called my mother to come, as we all sensed that this would be the epic final fight. The fight to put it all to rest, and once and for all, establish if Tito had what it took to defeat the dominant male.

The fight began.

Tito immediately began to rely on what experience he had gained. He attempted to circle around the dominant male, spurring him in the back. This jolted the dominant rooster forward, but it didn't injure him. He was able to do an about-face and faced Tito again. The dominant male was not a slouch either. He knew how to fight, and this battle would last a long time.

The dominant male, in an attempt to get to Tito's eyes, flapped his wings extra hard and twice as much, and tried to spear Tito in the face. Tito was quick on his feet and avoided disaster. They then began to go back and forth, trying to get the better of each other, spearing and spurring each other. At one point, it seemed as if Tito had gotten a good lick in, but the dominant male remained unfazed.

Tito tried all he knew. He didn't give up. He even attempted to try a strategy where he turned as if to run, then when the dominant male gave chase, he quickly turned around, now already in position, to spear the dominant male. The dominant male, now unable to react as quick, was speared once in the chest. This knocked the dominant male back, and Tito rushed in for another spur. The next spur missed, and Tito and the dominant male began to spear each other equally again.

The battle raged on. What felt like at least nine to ten minutes, they were in the yard, fighting for dominance. Suddenly and miraculously, Tito got in a good spear. It knocked the dominant male down, but he quickly got back up. It was apparent, however, that something had changed.

The dominant male was getting tired.

Tito on the other hand was in prime shape and was still spurring and spearing, as angry as ever. Spearing for the injustice of his younger days. Spearing for the bullying he once received at the sharp beaks of everyone in the yard. Perhaps even spearing from the love he got from my mother. I can't say for sure. All I know is we witnessed the tables beginning to turn on the dominant male. The dominant male began to not be able to jump as high. He began to slowly fade. He was still flapping vigorously, but now Tito's flaps were seen as more powerful. Tito was knocking back the dominant male, and the dominant male was struggling to keep up.

Tito was winning.

After what looked like another five minutes of fighting, the miracle finally happened.

Tito knocked back the dominant male, and the dominant male, unable to take the next blow, stepped back, and for the first time in a long time, he turned around and fled. Fled for his life, for he was wise enough to know, that he was losing and would be killed, should he continue.

Upon seeing this, Tito gave chase. He chased the now beaten male around the yard for a little bit, still very much angry. He was letting all his rage out, and the dominant male could not deal with it. When we realized what was happening, we all shouted "Yes!

Tito did it!" We were so happy! Tito had beaten the dominant male.

Tito was the new, official, King of the Yard.

Now victorious, Tito stopped chasing the now defeated rooster. He stood still, arched his neck back, and crowed. Now, with no longer any other challengers to face him, his crow stood out strongly amongst everyone else. The defeated old king did not crow back in defiance. He instead hid at the other end of the yard, out of sight from Tito.

My mother was the happiest she had ever been when dealing with yard fowls, I tell you. She had seen Tito, her baby, win and become king. She was so proud of him, and she kept calling out "Tito! Tito!". We were all very happy. Happy indeed, for this once baby chick who was so weak and bullied, now finally, has become the one and only king.

* * * * *

Tito enjoyed his success and began to mate with all the viable hens. No one contested this, for he had earned his title. He was king of the yard, and all respected him. Sometimes, he flexed his power and chased around the now defeated old king, and did it to show that he had overpowered him. Sometimes, my father would get mad at him puffing up his chest and crowing after chasing around the old male, and he would begin to chase Tito away if he felt Tito was being too cruel. My mother didn't like that and told my father to leave him alone, as he has endured a lot to get where he was. We all mostly agreed.

And thus, with satisfaction, I am pleased to tell you that the story of the chicken's life is now told.

I once again attest to you that everything I stated here is true and fact and that this all happened right before me, as I grew up in the country.

As I end my story, I leave you with a small joke. After Tito would chase away all the other younger roosters who were now up and coming, even I would sometimes get slightly annoyed, and I would tell Tito to not be so cocky. Sometimes it seemed as if he stopped listening to us, now that he was king. I would then wait till he was chasing around all the hens or young males, and begin to chase all of them around. Male and female alike.

It did not matter about royalty or who was king. It didn't matter if you were young, old, a chick, or a mother hen. It didn't matter how strong you were compared to the other hens or the other males.

When humans chase fowls down, they all flee. Rooster, young hen, older mother hen young male, baby chicks, everyone.

This I found to be quite funny, for we had witnessed immense battles for power, and dominance, yet to the human, the fowl was but a small bird livestock, who we reared for meat and eggs.

Before such power, no fowl could stand a chance.

Sometimes I would laugh as they all fled. *Fleeing for their life* from one human. Sometimes, however, I stopped chasing them, as I would have a single thought.

The thought was, just as these chickens run from humans, who hold power over them all, *what if* God, annoyed by our arrogance, began chasing us away and scaring the living daylights out of us? This was often a sobering thought, and whenever I had that thought, I would stop chasing them around, and left the poor chickens alone.

The Meeting

*"You never know where your actions in life may lead, all you
can do is follow your heart, follow your heart indeed. "*

It was a chance meeting, him and her. She often
walked by the park and always admired the
flowers. That is, what little we have *left* in the
cities nowadays. Natural growing, beautiful flowers,
that often don't grow by themselves.

He saw her walking one day and knew he wanted
to say hello. She spotted him walking towards her
and thought he was fairly handsome. He initially
walked past her, and she was disappointed because
she was hoping for a smile or some gesture to show
his interest. However, he walked past her. But then,
he and stopped and said: *"Excuse me."*.

That was it. They met. They fell in love. It was a whirlwind romance. They went on trips together. They spent many, many hours together in the same room, talking of life, the future, and all that the world contains.

He was a noble man and a good person, seemingly possessing ambitions to find a way to right the wrongs of the world. Poverty, crime, pollution, he wanted to fix it all. She was herself, a lover of all things beautiful and fair, but was very realistic and practical. Combined, they shared a strong sense of justice and right vs wrong, but with a shared love of beauty, and things that made the world a better place.

Indeed, the world needed more couples like them, for the world was becoming a very bad place. All over could be found pollution and rank nastiness. People stopped caring about the planet, once it was found out that the planet could not be sustained for the next five hundred years due to global warming. They polluted and destroyed. Besides this, corporations continued their greed, all the while lapping up what little resources the planet had left.

Worst of all, the attitudes and minds of the people were one of apathy and genuine loss of interest in nature, the environment, or the planet as a whole. People simply did not care anymore. For good measure, things weren't looking up for them. The planet had, but a short time left. People were essentially living, hopeless and apathetic, with no direct line to the future, or to the meaning and purpose of life.

She was a Botanist. She loved to study flowers in particular and had many plants and flowers in the home where they both lived. He was a scientist. He often would talk of his experiments and what should be done to fix global warming, and what could be done to save the planet.

At times, they argued. Upon seeing the way people treated the environment and watched as grown adults would sometimes trample on small gardens and destroy flowers she planted in the dirt along the streets and places she frequented, she argued that she should be allowed to make it such that only flowers and certain species of plants should be in certain areas, away from people's influence. The man, however, argued that it was not the fact that people lived amongst plant life, it was that people just didn't care anymore.

Despite the occasional disagreement, they eventually got married and had a baby. The baby was named *Nevada*. Her mother named her so because her father always talked about turning the desert land in Nevada into an oasis, where they could plant and grow trees and have wildlife flourish. He always felt that America, along with other countries in the world, wasted a lot of its land and that the extra, unused areas could be harnessed to make the world a better place.

As baby Nevada grew up, she shared a strong love for nature herself, but more so, she seemed to love people. She loved playing with children she just met, and she was always comfortable around strange adults she never met. She never cried, even when a strange man or woman held her, and always just looked to ensure her mother or father was around. As long as they were close by, she never feared.

When she was ten years old, her father was diagnosed with Cancer. They did everything they could for him, but after two long years of battling the disease, he succumbed. Before he died, he would take little Nevada on his lap and tell her all about the planet, and how much he loved it, and that she should do everything in her power to try to save it. He told her to always take care of her mother. He also taught her that trusting others, while not a bad thing in of itself, it must be done with tact, for not everyone has her best interests in mind.

Her father would teach her many more lessons during his sickness, and Nevada would remember these lessons for the rest of her life.

A very important lesson Nevada's father taught her was that self-sacrifice can sway the tide of distrust. As people see that you are willing to self-sacrifice for good to be achieved, and you do it with sincerity, it would have an effect on people's minds, and some may be encouraged by the bravery you display and may join and support you on your endeavors. He cautioned her that this must be done with *great sincerity*, for if people were to detect even a hint of non-genuine motives, you would risk losing people's trust forever.

Soon after, her father passed. Her mother became saddened, and much quieter. She no longer kept many plants and flowers in the house. She no longer sought out places to plant flowers to beautify the area. She would still take care of a few rare species of flowers, but most of her time was spent home by herself in the house, taking care of Nevada.

Despite this, Nevada's mother would take her occasionally to the park, and show her different plant and flower species and told her all about how amazing each one was. She did this from the moment Nevada's father died. Now, twelve, she could better understand the more intricate nuances of different environments, and how they affect different species of plants and the terrains they lived in. She also taught Nevada as much extra knowledge she could teach her about Geography and why the Earth was so complex and beautiful.

When Nevada was fourteen, her mother took her to a park and showed her a specific set of flowers. She said these flowers were rare to grow in nature without help, but here they were, struggling to grow still yet.

She taught Nevada with this lesson, that she should never give up, and that for things like this, you sacrifice everything you have, to save whatever it is, for the rarer the flower, the harder it has to work to survive. This, she said was true of the whole planet, for science taught them that the whole planet was rare, even though it was discovered that they only had about five hundred years left and people had lost hope. It was still beautiful, despite the levels of apathy and hopelessness seen in people as they went about their daily lives.

Nevada was growing into a wonderful, smart, and empathetic child. She often helped others, and always took care of her mother, as her father had asked her to. She made friends, did well in school, and never got into trouble or harmed anyone.

One day, as Nevada was walking home from school, she met a man, who was standing and looking at the overpass of cars driving along the highway. She watched as he climbed up onto the overpass ledge and lifted his foot to jump into oncoming traffic.

Nevada shouted *"No! Wait!"*

This startled the man, and he turned around to see Nevada running up to him and grab him and pull him off the ledge. The man surprised that a little girl was brave and smart enough to realize what was happening, he sat on the ground next to her and looked at her.

Nevada was crying. He then finally spoke.

"Why are you crying, my dear?" He asked.

"Because you wanted to kill yourself!" Nevada answered, sobbing.

"My dear, you don't even know me. You don't know what I've done,"

"It doesn't matter! I didn't want to see you die like that!"

"Why do you even care?"

"Because, if you die, somebody, somewhere will be sad. I don't want that. You are worth saving. Everyone is."

"Who taught you that my dear?"

"My Mother. She taught me that everyone is worth saving and that I should do everything I could to save them."

"Your mother sounds like a very wonderful person."

"She is. I love her so much. Now please, promise you won't do this again!"

"Ok, ok, I won't do it again. Now please, stop crying and let me go, will you?"

Nevada was hanging onto the man's legs like the dickens. When he said that, she relaxed her grip and let the man go. They both stood up and promised he wouldn't do it again, and started to walk away.

"What's your name, sir?" Nevada asked. She was always taught to learn names and be polite.

"Mr. Cent. You can call me Mr. C if you like."

"Ok Mr. C, my name is Nevada, and remember, you promised never to do that again, so I will hold you to that, ok?"

"Sure my dear." Mr. Cent replied,

"I promise I won't do that again."

* * * * *

When Nevada got home, she ran to her mother, who was in the back yard, watering a few flowers. She told her mother all that happened, and her mother was at first shocked, but glad she was ok.

"Are you hurt anywhere Nevada?"

"No Mom, I'm ok, but I saved that man's life!" I wish I could tell everyone I know!"*

"Well, just be careful ok baby? Try to avoid getting into situations like that anymore. It's too dangerous. I don't want you to get hurt."

"Ok, Mom. I will try."

Nevada's mother smiled at her and told her to go change her clothes from school and do her homework. As she walked back inside the house, Nevada's mom called her.

"Nevada."

"Yes, Mom?"

"You did a wonderful thing today. You saved someone's life. What you did today, may not seem like much, but you never know the effect of saving one person's life. You should always remember that, ok?"

"Yes, Mom. I will."

"Now go, change those clothes, come back downstairs when you're done your homework, and I will have dinner ready."

Nevada ran back into the house. She nodded her head.

"Yes, Mom. Love you!"

Her mom looked at the flowers and kept watering them.

"I know baby. I love you too."

The *Self-Help* Guru

"Wits match with wit, jealousy and envy run high, he is popular, handsome, and rich, he makes the ladies gossip and sigh."

H e was a smart and handsome man. When he spoke, everyone around him knew that he was intelligent. Noble, tall, and well-spoken, he added charisma, charm, and an excellent wardrobe to the package, and it was complete. An impressive male. The stuff of GQ dreams.

He moved into the area quite silently, as no one really knew who he was, but at the same time, when they approached him or spoke to him, the people living there felt like they knew him for many years, and that he was reliable, trustworthy and an overall good guy. He was very confident and magnanimous. This helped boost his impressive status, and the neighbors almost felt proud to live near someone this grand, despite not knowing much about this new man.

It wasn't until several of the ladies began to stop and stare at this impressive specimen, that their husbands began to inquire as to what he really did. Said one: "*What's this guy do anyway?*" He only asked this out of an effort to get into the new guy's business. Of course, out of jealousy. John, the guy who asked this, was a jealous, insecure weasel. But even I won't lie. I won't stand by and watch my girl staring at some dude, heck, no one should. Albeit, I would reprimand her instead, and not focus on the guy. But that's me personally. I don't play that game.

I actually liked the new guy. See, I'm the type of person when I see someone essentially looking and living better than me, I want to get close to them, and learn their secrets to make *myself* a better person. Not to hate on them. This is how I always lived my life. Whether in school, work, or common interactions in life, we all should seek out people who are successful and mimic their behavior, in an effort to improve ourselves and improve our skills. This is the whole purpose behind having a mentor as well.

The neighborhood had planned a Sunday afternoon barbeque and invited everyone to come. The men and woman in the neighborhood hoped that the new guy would attend, for different reasons, of course. The women hoped they could now get a chance to interact with, and have conversations with the new handsome neighbor, now in a socially acceptable way, but the men had hoped to use this opportunity to now pry into the new neighbor's life, looking for flaws or weaknesses to one day exploit.

Not one to back *down* from an obvious challenge or trap, the new guy attended the barbeque. He showed up, only slightly late, to garner all eyes on him as he walked into the small event. He was as mentioned before, very handsome, tall and dressed casually, but clean, with a pink polo shirt and a new pair of jeans. He looked fun, sporty, and hip. The ladies loved it. They each greeted him rather cheerfully, with their husbands standing close by their sides, like jealous little rats.

Little rats they were, for they never approached him at the event unless he was speaking to one of their wives first. Honestly, they were pathetic. I'm not saying homeboy was right, now that I look back on everything, but these weaselly, wimpy, simpy, pathetic men made me laugh.

Be confident in your relationship, and with your girl. If she is making you insecure, or you have reason to doubt, then you might as well be single. It's simple really. But that's just me.

Once they felt confident enough to go through with the plan, the men gathered and went in for their attack. The new guy saw it coming a mile away and excused himself to get something to eat. This was genius, for how could you attack and bombard someone with hundreds of questions, if they have a mouthful of food? It just wasn't polite, as the person would be forced to answer while chewing, and this was seen as uncouth and bad manners to do this to a person while they were trying to eat. Hence, the men had to wait.

It was a small group of guys, maybe no more than four or five of us total. I was among the guys in the group, but I didn't feel like them. The new guy had spoken to my girl and said hi, but I let her know quickly with a simple glance, that I wasn't messing around. Besides, I was always doing things to improve myself, so my girl was quite happy with me.

Also, I lay the smackdown in bed. So…yeah. I wasn't playing that game. She was NOT looking at anyone else, not while I was in the picture. I tell you that much.

These men, however, not so much. They were some sappy ass guys, who were pathetic, out of shape and silly, with wives and children, only because they made good money and their wives were used to the lifestyle. In any case, they wanted to pry into this man's life like a drill burring down into a piece of wood. They didn't care how silly and weak and insecure they looked *(and they looked very insecure)*, as long as they got what they wanted.

They were like a thirsty dog trying to lap up some water, while his master beat him to run away. They were so thirsty, that despite the beating, they would take it, as long as they got to drink that water.

Their plan delayed for a moment, they had to disperse and wait, for the new guy was eating.

But that's when the new guy saw her. That's when he saw his downfall.

She was the wife of the president of the homeowner's association. She was extremely gorgeous. She always wore a pair of trendy glasses that looked more like a fashion statement than a necessity for her to see. She had natural auburn brown hair that grew to shoulder length. She always wore her hair in a bun, and let just a little down to the side, making her look like a sexy nerdy teacher. I was married, and my wife was cute, but damn if I didn't wish my wife looked like her too. If I got the chance, I would *"xyz"* her myself if you know what I mean? Shoots. I'm not gonna even lie. Anyway, she was walking by with the president, and when the new guy saw her, he knew at that moment that he was hooked and a goner.

She hadn't seen him yet, but she knew about him from all the chatter in the neighborhood. After all, the ladies talked about the "new guy" relentlessly. She had heard so many rumors, she was already impressed with him, despite having never met him. The president himself had met him and was impressed by him, so that fueled her curiosity to see what type of man he was even more.

After the new guy finished eating his meal, he quickly went and cleaned up and made his way towards the direction the wife of the president was standing. He had to get to know her. He *needed* to get to know her.

Here was the group of husbands first chance. They hadn't noticed that the new neighbor was heading towards the wife of the president, but they knew he was on the move, so they didn't want to waste the opportunity. Finally, they would corner him and get answers to all their burning questions. They would finally get to question him and get a chance to grasp what *exactly* his intentions were.

The new guy made his move. He waited until she had stepped away from her husband as he spoke to a few of the other ladies about some association business, and he approached her and introduced himself.

"Hi, I've never met you before, my name is Mark, what's your name?"

"Oh hello, you must be the new neighbor that moved in, I'm Alice. Nice to meet you."

"Pleasure's mine. What a beautiful name for a beautiful woman. Do you live in the house down the street?"

"Oh! I see what everyone was talking about. So flattering. You have a way with the ladies, I see. I have to keep an eye on you."

"Really? And what do they say about me?"

"That he's handsome and charming and very well-spoken. He's also very charismatic and…"

"Well, I am most of those things…"

"Confident, I see as well. Hmm, I better watch myself then…"

"Haha, maybe…I do have that way with the ladies, as you said. Best to stay away and keep your guard with me. I can be addicting…"

"Oh, I see. Tell me more then…"

Alice was loving it. She was flattered that the new handsome neighbor was flirting with her, and she was also impressed that he was about as much as the other ladies had said, and even a bit more. He was funny, indeed charming, but down to earth, and able to carry an amusing conversation.

The new guy was a pro. He got closer to her and even began touching her shoulders from time to time. This was a tactic to get her comfortable with him, and it was working. She began playfully tapping him on the arm as well, as her defenses slowly came down. Meh. Didn't seem like she had any up to begin with, anyway. But that's just me.

As they began to get deeper into their conversation, the men struck. They went in for the kill.

Mark replied to her, trying to make the conversation a little more sensual.

"Well, I can be naughty…"

"A naughty what?" Asked one of the husbands from the group of insecure men.

"Hey, how are you John, didn't see you there, buddy."

He was engrossed in the eyes of Alice and didn't see the men approaching from the side. Gotta stay focused when you playing this game. Enemies can attack from anywhere, bro.

"Sorry to jump in, but that conversation was sounding so interesting, I had to join!"

John, one of the husbands in our group thought he was slick.

"Haha, well, I was telling Alice here, that I can be a naughty individual when I have to be, but I was referring to my mischievous side..."

"Ah, ok, no problem Mark! Hey, aren't we all a bit naughty? Huh? Huh? Am I right? Hahaha!"

Dude was making me sick. He thought he had Mark on the ropes. Well, if I'm being fair, *he kinda did.*

John continued the cock-block.

"So Alice, what about your husband? Did he disappear and leave you here amongst the wolves? Haha, that guy…"

This was smart. What the weaselly John did, was subtly remind Alice that she was getting too flirty with this new guy and that she did in fact, have a husband, who was present there at the event. To me, I wonder if that was something she needed to even be reminded of. Hmm…

Also, in addition to this, it was a low blow and a subtle insult to the new guy Mark, who was getting too close to the President's wife, and they wanted to end that nonsense, quick. Guy had too much of the ladies swooning as it was.

The comment that the weaselly husband made seemed to snap Alice out of her flirty bubble, and she seemed to come to her senses. She addressed the rest of the guys in the group, and flashed Mark a quick smile, and excused herself to go stand where her husband was.

Now the full-on assault could begin.

One of the other husbands, Tom, had jumped in. He was gonna show this new guy who was boss.

"Say, Mark, was it? How are you, my friend?"

"I'm doing great Tom, how are you?"

"Good! Good! I hope you enjoyed my wife's casserole. She makes a mean casserole eh?"

"Certainly, it's some of the best I've had. You're a lucky man, Tom. I wish I had a wife who cooked that well!"

John, the first husband that approached him then spoke up again.

"So you don't have a wife? Not married?"

"Haha, no, still living the single life John, but maybe one day."

"Ah, I see. What's a handsome man like you not locked down as yet huh? What are you waiting for?"

"Well, you know. Life gets in the way sometimes. But when I find that special person, I will lock her down myself!"

Mark had attempted to make a guy joke, hoping to ease the tension of the group of husbands, who clearly had it out for him. He knew it was better not to bring too much attention and scrutiny on himself, because that would greatly hinder his work, and what he wanted to do. It would also start false rumors, or in other words, damaging rumors that could ruin his clean built-up intrigue and rep. He realized that he needed to do something to ease their fears. Let them know he was human, like them.

Sadly, this did not work. Tom, the other guy who was present in the group, spoke up.

"Haha, well, you can't have Alice! Haha! I know she is a looker, but she's married, my man! Haha!"

This was a pot-shot at Mark, and letting him know that they saw what he was trying to do, and it was a signal that they would cock-block him any chance they got or in any way they knew. I mean, yeah, homegirl was married. It wasn't right to be looking at another guy's girl. But if she was interested in him, as I found out later, then who are we to stop or interfere with that?

Mark was not stupid. As a matter of fact, the guy was a genius in my eyes. It was then that Mark smiled. This was no ordinary smile, no. I saw something twinkle in his eyes, as he looked at Tom, and John and the rest of us. I watched as the formulation of an ingenious plan came to his mind, and I watched as an emotion burst up, silently, to his eyes. No one else saw it, but I did. I was watching him intently, and as I said, I secretly admired the guy. Heck, I wanted to be *like* him.

What it was, was that Mark got angry.

It was not anger, that you see, as when people show emotion. It was an anger of determination and intellect. How dare these weaselly ass men insult him? How dare they threaten and try to embarrass him? He had done nothing to them. It was clear jealousy and nothing more. He had flirted a bit here and there with a few of the wives, but he had not touched or gone a single extra step with any of the other ladies. If he was handsome and carried himself well, and dressed well, this was not his fault if the ladies liked him, admired him, or stared at him. It was *their* fault.

And as far as I was concerned, Mark was right.

Men have a responsibility to keep their wives impressed with them, just as we require women to *always* be attractive and beautiful. No one wants a fat-bellied slob, just as no one wants an ugly, unkempt, out of shape wife, no matter what you *say*. People want to see beauty. It's a law of life. Take it for what you will, but it is the truth. I know it. *You know it.*

Mark had been insulted. These men had come, interfered with him, cock-blocked a conversation that was getting interesting and had now insulted him.

He would get his revenge. And man, that revenge was awesome. I was there, and I saw it, and all I can say, is that it was a shame that it's all over now. I would have cheered him on all the way.

Mark began to speak. This genius of a man began to speak. Here is where it all began. The plan to get his revenge. It spiraled from there, and I don't think Mark planned it that way, but maybe he did.

"Yeah! You're right my man! She is cute no doubt. Haha, a lucky guy the president is, huh?"

The men hadn't expected him to respond in this agreeable way. They had expected him to be embarrassed and speechless, and then when caught off guard, they would ask him his business, and under shock, he would be socially forced to spill the beans. Haha. Those men did not know who they were messing with.

"Yeah, she is gorgeous right?" Tom responded, not realizing he was already ensnared, caught, and executed. All in one single question. This was *exactly* the answer that Mark wanted. *Got em.*

"Yeah, but she isn't as cute as your wife? Am I right? Huh?" nudging Tom on the shoulder.

This was genius, as Mark instantaneously turned the conversation back on Tom. After all, are you gonna stand there and admire another man's wife yourself? While telling another guy that he shouldn't? I'm telling you; Mark was a genius. Damn, I loved that man.

"Yeah, that's right…no, yeah…no my wife is hotter…of course"

I smiled in my heart. These men were fools. Mark would go on to psychologically man-handle them.

"I agree! Haha! No lady should be hotter than your wife, right!"

John realized that Tom was on the ropes. He was a bit shrewder than Tom, so he recognized that Tom was cornered. There was nothing left to do, but to just come right out and launch the *final attack.*

There was now no longer any reason to delay. If they did, they knew that Mark would find a way to get out of it, and they had stood and talked with him long enough to know that Mark was not a stupid man. In fact, they knew they were dealing with high caliber stuff right there, and knew they had to act quickly.

"So Mark," John jumped in to say. *"What do you do for a living?"*

This was their whole point. This single question would direct the whole conversation and give them what they needed to know about him. You see, the men knew all the businesses in the surrounding area, so if Mark worked for any one of them, they would be able to get all the info they needed and then some. They would pry into his life, and get every single detail. Then when they found what they needed, that is, some form of weakness or flaw, then they would humble his handsome ass, and bring him down to earth with the rest of the men who were fat, big-bellied, and grossly flawed.

However, unbeknownst to the group of men, this was indeed the one question Mark was waiting for. Haha. I admit, even I was taken aback and caught off guard with his answer. I didn't know at the time where he was going with it but looking back now, it was pure, unadulterated genius. You guys don't know. I'm telling you. I wish I was Mark so bad. If I had that guy's looks and intelligence? I would be a damn politician. Or a millionaire or something.

"Well, I'm a Self-Help Guru."

"A self-help guru?" John asked. Completely taken aback by that answer.

"Uh-huh. That's right."

"Oh, ok. So what does a self-help guru do?" John was so surprised by the answer that he didn't stop to think about the definition of the words in the actual name.

See what I mean? These guys were idiots. Mark realized it as well.

"Well, a self-help guru is someone who gives life advice and coaches people to become their better selves."

"Oh, oh. I see." Tom, now recovered from his cornered stupor from earlier, joined in.

"Do you work from home then?" Tom asked.

"Well, I can, but I mostly work everywhere and, in all places, so in a sense, my office is the world!" Mark replied.

He was weaving the web that would ensnare us all.

"Oh, that sounds pretty cool bro." I said. I wanted to join in on the conversation too.

"Yeah Michael, it's pretty amazing. I help people all over the world, and help improve their lives for the better."

John jumped back in. He didn't know it, but he was at the precipice of Mark's web. All he needed was a push.

"So Mark, how much money do you make with that job?"

John couldn't help it. He was the most jealous of all the men. You don't come right out and ask that. It's just not polite. I mean, sure, guys can talk about it, but it has to be the right context. Just blurting it out at the wrong time is a clear sign of prying into someone's business and life. However, as Mark foresaw this, he was ready.

"Well, I can make as much or as little as I want. It really all depends."

"Oh? Depends on what?" They were too stupid to *not* ask.

"You know, different factors. Let's say, one year, I want to purchase a car. I can work more to obtain the finances necessary to buy the car within a month or two, or if I don't need anything, I can just work a little here and there, just enough to live, eat, pay taxes, enjoy life, etc."

"Oh, I see," Tom answered. *"so you are freelance?"*

"Well, not necessarily. It is a full-on occupational choice." *It's just that I can make as little or as much money as I choose."*

This seemed to interest the men, and they inquired more. This is what Mark wanted. He wanted to hook them. After all, it was a part of his plan.

"So as a Self-Help Guru, I can travel to any part of the world, and people pay me large sums of money to help them be successful and change their lives. Bill used me only last year as a "wellness checkup" of sorts. I mean, he already is a billionaire…but…"

Haha! Mark was subtly dropping names. I love it!

"Bill? Who? You mean Bill Gates?"

"Well, I'm not supposed to say anything, you know. It's privileged info, but yeah, I advise him from time to time too."

"What? No way. Bullshit." John replied.

He was skeptical. But Mark was prepared. Dude was always prepared. He took out his phone and played a video of himself standing next to Bill Gates at a charitable event and shaking his hand. Unbeknownst to the men, it was for the previous company he had worked for, and they were sponsoring a philanthropic event that Mr. Gates had attended to garner large donations for a cause. Mark had nothing to do with it. It was solely because Mark worked there and was handsome, the photographer thought it would look good for a media shot. Mark got access to the footage and kept it on his phone for just a time as this.

"Listen, I have other famous clients, and I can prove it, but you see, I don't want to go to jail guys."

This was enough. This was all it took. It caused the group of men to temporarily forget their objective, their goal. They were simply too impressed.

They had fallen over the precipice. They were in Mark's territory now. We all were. We were done. This was too convincing.

"So, you advise big-name clients only?" Tom asked.

"Well, no my friend! That wouldn't be helpful to everyone if I just helped super-rich people who are already successful. I also help every day, common people. I examine your life and give you advice that works almost ninety to ninety-five percent of the time. Of course, it all depends on you, but my formula has been proven and it is successful."

"And you make a lot of money doing this?"

"As much or as little as I want. I have full control."

"Really?" John asked, still a little doubtful.

"What do you guys think?" Mark answered, then raised his hands and pointed at himself.

This was all it took. The men stopped and thought about it for a bit. It was a quick few seconds, but you could see all the men's minds going. Thinking, analyzing. Making sense of it all. You see, Mark was a fine specimen, and all the men in the group knew it. He was handsome and he was well dressed. He had just bought the new house down the street and moved in, without any help or need of anyone. He was popular with the ladies. He carried himself well. *Very well.*

This added up to making Mark's story super convincing. After all, wouldn't it make sense he was successful if he was advising billionaires and other people on how to be successful? He was using his own formula, and to the guys in the group, that shit was working splendidly. They had now completely forgotten about their plan, and now, fully entrapped into Mark's web, they asked him the final question that would seal their fate.

"So what's the formula?" John asked.

These suckers couldn't help it.

"Well, that's a secret, John! Haha! Can't tell you that so easily! It's how I make my living!"

"Oh, ok, yeah, I understand that."

Mark paused for a second and appeared to be thinking about it and squinting his eyes. Looking back, he wasn't thinking about anything. He already had the plan worked out.

"Haha, you guys are cool. Tell you what, I wasn't going to bring this up, but I was gonna start advertising my services and taking consults. I didn't know how the neighborhood felt

about it, so I was gonna wait to get to know everyone first, but since you guys are so nice, I can tell you now. I also do the occasional speech, but you guys won't be interested."

Haha. Mark was the psychology king.

"Well, why not buddy?" Tom answered. *"I wouldn't mind a consult."*

"Really?" Mark replied.

"Sure, why not? I can make time next week."

I wasn't gonna be left behind. Shoots. I spoke up too.

"Hey Mark, me too. Count me in."

My response seemed to spur on all the guys in the group as well. They all started asking for consults and asked how much it would cost.

Mark smiled. We were all fools. But I'm not mad at all. I liked and respected him a lot. And honestly, it served these men right. You don't treat a new person like that without getting to know them first. It's wrong. What they got, they got.

"Well, I usually charge two-fifty per hour for my consulting services, but for you guys, I can knock off fifty as a

*discount and charge you guys just two hundred an hour. I do
have other packages too."*

"What other packages?" Tom felt that $200/hour
was a little steep. This is what Mark wanted anyway.

*"Well, I do give speeches to large crowds, and I charge
only one hundred per person per ticket for admission. That
way, it is much cheaper on everyone, and everyone gets to hear
the excellent advice that changes their lives, together. I make a
two-hour speech, and everyone only pays one hundred each.
The ticket prices are essentially used to cover the venue fees,
and mic and sound system rental, and I take a transparent
cut off of the top, and the rest is used to serve refreshments and
snacks, etc. I like that setup better, as I don't make a lot of
excess money, and I get to help everyone instead. Plus, it is
cheaper than consulting individually at my regular rate. It's a
win-win for everyone."*

This sounded excellent to the men, who when
they heard it, felt that that was the better deal, and at
the same time, they felt it was safer to be together
with everyone, so in case he spoke some form of
bullcrap, the entire audience would catch it, and
expose him for the *fraud* he was. Or, if things were
going well, as they knew Mark was a smooth talker,
and could easily sway the ladies to his side, they

would begin to be obnoxious, and disagree and boo him. This would throw him off his guard in front of all, and make him look, at the very bare minimum, like a fool. They secretly all felt this was good, and so they agreed that this was better than a single consult, and they would be interested in this more.

"Really guys? Are you interested? If so, we can do something next weekend. It would be amazing. I have some pointers and tips that I already see can help you guys. It would be my pleasure to share."

John replied to him.

"Yeah Mark, let's do it. Tell you what, I will work out all the details for you. We will collect all the funds and everything. You just sit back, prepare that awesome speech, and we will handle the details. How does that sound?"

John felt happy that he thought he had found a way to finally defeat Mark, and so he was so happy that he became generous.

"Oh ok. Sure. Are you sure John? I mean, if it isn't too much trouble."

Haha. Suckers.

"No trouble at all! I can talk to the president, as he knows the guy who lives a few miles away that has a small

restaurant venue party place that would work perfectly. Plus, you are our neighbor now, I would be honored to help out with this. Don't you worry. When all is set, I will bring you your funds, and everything. You just prepare that killer speech for us."

"Oh ok, great! You got it, John. And hey, I will prepare something extra special. I guarantee it. You will have your socks knocked off."

"Awesome! Ok, great! We're doing this then." John replied.

He felt he was the leader of our group. What a fool. He was not the leader. Not of me, at least. I just played along to ensure I was always in the loop amongst these idiots.

"Alright fellas, let's leave Mark alone eh? We bombarded him with enough questions for the day."

"See you, Mark." We all said as we walked away.

As I was walking away, I looked back at Mark and nodded my head and smiled. He was smiling back and he nodded his head back. I knew it even then. My feelings told me this was not at all what it appeared to be. It was almost as if he knew I had a suspicion, but knew I wouldn't *interfere.*

Hell no, I wouldn't. I was gonna see this thing *through*.

And so would Mark.

The *Self-Help* Guru II

"A gift wrapped in impressive paper does not make it true,
sometimes we must look past the sparkle, for a clearer point
of view. What we think is worth sacrificing our true
happiness for, is simply a sham; for you throw your
happiness out the door."

The rest of the weekend went by quickly and John began to make plans and take care of the venue for the coming Sunday's speech by Mark. He had invited the whole neighborhood to join, and even put up a portion of his own money, and this made the ticket prices slightly cheaper for everyone else. It was supposed to be roughly ninety to a hundred people in attendance, and as such, the ticket prices would be a total of roughly ten grand or more if everyone showed up.

John worked out the details and even got the venue free from the owner after speaking with the president. Total costs for the sound system were free, and also the refreshments were also free, as many of the wives, upon hearing that Mark was to give a speech, and who he was, and the clientele he managed, they offered to cook and make food for the event for free. Excitement was building, and people began to look forward to the event that coming Sunday.

That Wednesday morning, I was outside taking an early morning jog, when I spotted Alice. She was walking briskly, then jogging here and there. I saw her and I said hello, as I ran in the opposite direction to her. She smiled at me and waved me down to stop.

I stopped and ran back like a glad little pup to talk to this gorgeous woman and exchange my greetings. We spoke a little bit about how life was going, and what we were doing, and then the topic fell on Mark.

"So what do you think of him, Mike?" She liked to call me Mike.

I didn't mind. My wife was a little perturbed by it though.

"I mean, he seems like a nice guy. Honestly, I like him. Well, in truth, I like him a lot."

"Oh, Mike, I didn't know you went that way. I always thought you were a handsome guy, but you were taken, so I never flirted with you like that. It's a good thing since you're not into "my kind". Are you gonna come out to your wife soon? Huh? Haha!"

Damn. This woman loved to tease and flirt. She was beautiful and she *knew* it.

"Haha, Alice. You know exactly which way I swing…heck if you were single, and I was single, this would be a whole different conversation. I'm telling you right now girl."

She smiled at me and laughed. I shook my head at her and smiled back. I didn't play that, son. You can't come after me like *that*. I was no slouch, you know. But I knew the game. I pivoted back.

"So I saw you and Mark talking the other day at the Barbeque. Mark is a handsome dude; I give him that."

"Yeah, he's put together. I like that. Such a good dresser too. Can you believe he coaches Billionaires and stuff? Wow."

Homegirl was impressed. *Of course* she was. Mark was at this time, on everybody's mouths, including my own. Shoots. I'm not gonna even lie.

"Yeah, I wish I had his job!" I replied.

"Yeah, me too. Heck, his girlfriend must be lucky."

Heheh, she was trying to fish info from me. These girls think they're so slick. I played along. I gave her what she wanted.

"I don't think he mentioned he had a girlfriend…"

"Oh, that's right…oh ok, no big deal anyway"

Yeah, uh-huh. You act like you didn't want to know that. Girls are funny.

"Well, you take care Mike, maybe you should have met me first before your wife. We could have done something. Don't tell her I said that! Haha!"

Ever the flirt, she had to get her last lick in. She smiled at me.

"Girl, you better stop playing. I might take you seriously. You know I don't play around. See you later."

"I know. You're a good man. I always liked and respected you. Any girl would be lucky to have you, Mike."

Damn straight. She knew what time it was.

I smiled back. *"Ok see you. Oh, you coming this weekend, right?"*

"Yeah, I'll be there. I can't wait to hear Mark give that speech. He seems like a very smart guy. I know it will be amazing…"

Just then, someone patted me from behind on the shoulder. It was Mark.

"Hey Michael, how are you, my friend!"

Mark was up early that morning and looked out his window and saw us walking by. That dude was not gonna waste a good opportunity to follow up on his goals. I saw it and instantly realized.

I'm gonna tell you right now. I am *not* a cock-blocker. No matter what. I respect men, and I demand respect myself. I had my small say, and it was time to give another dude a chance. Such is the respect among men. Plus, if I'm being honest, I couldn't shoot my shot, but Mark? Hell yeah, I was rooting for him.

"Hey, buddy! Looking forward to this weekend! Knock us dead brother!" I said as I turned to jog away and give the man his time.

"You got it, Michael!" He replied as I jogged away.

About ten steps or so away, I turned around to look at them. Alice was lit up like a Christmas tree and was flirting away like a butterfly. She was smiling and touching Mark on the arms, and they were having a great time. He had said something low, and I couldn't hear it clearly, but it was something like sweaty, but beautiful or something like that, and she stepped back and did the gesture that shows like *"who me?"* and laughed.

At that moment, I looked at Mark, and he turned around and saw me looking at him, and this time he nodded first, and I smiled and nodded back.

Good guy.

Later in the week, on Friday afternoon, John had come by to collect my part of the ticket price. It was now eighty dollars each ticket for me and my wife, as he had put up a large sum of the total ticket costs, so everyone could feel happier knowing they got a good deal. I was one of the last people to hand in funds, and then we were gonna go by Mark's house to give the final details of the venue and give him his fees for the event.

I gave John my cut, and me, John and another guy from our group walked over to Mark's house.

Tom was still at work and didn't get home yet, but he had given his funds earlier in the week. When we got to Mark's house, he answered the door and let us in. He showed us his whole house. It was nice. He took us to his garage and showed us a light brown BMW. It looked amazing. It had a custom color paint job, and it was done well. I asked Mark if he would let me test drive it sometime. He said if we ever got some time, then sure.

His place was very nice. It was like a modern chic minimalist design. He kept pictures of art and had vases and collectible pieces everywhere on shelves and countertops. We knew that Mark had money. John realized that just from his house, he didn't need money. He could get money anytime he wanted.

John outlined the venue and all the minute details and what the seating arrangement would be like and the refreshments, everything. Mark said he would speak for one hour, then they could stop, take a break for a half-hour, get refreshments, then come back for the final hour. Depending on if everyone was willing, he had even prepared an extra thirty minutes of content for us as a bonus, if everyone wanted to stay longer to hear it.

Everyone thought that was a great idea, as two hours may go by rather quickly if things were going well, and having an extra thirty minutes of content was smart.

John handed over the full sum, a little over ten thousand dollars, and Mark thanked him and asked us if we wanted a beer and to watch a game together. I didn't mind, but John said he had to go finalize the details and make sure all was ready for the weekend.

I told Mark I would stay for a bit, then head home as my wife would be home soon.

John and the other guy left. I was waiting for this, as I wanted to talk to Mark one on one for a long time. Now was my chance. I went straight to business.

"Just promise me you won't look at Francine once you finish up with Alice bro!"

I let him know quickly that I was just here to *observe,* but not to interfere.

Mark laughed. He looked at me for like five seconds, trying to figure out if he could trust me. I raised my hands and gestured like *"come onnn"* and with that, he seemed to know that he could trust me.

After all, I wouldn't spoil his game. I wanted him to succeed. I really did. Sorry, *Mr. Homeowners Association President.*

"Bro, she is smoking hot."

I laughed out loud.

"I know! Shit! You are a lucky dude, son. I don't know how you do it, bro. I wish I had your finesse. I'm ok with my thing. I mean, I do my thing, but bro, you got these ladies going crazy over here! I don't know man. But you do you, brother. I am just a humble observer."

"Damn. I know she's married though. But I don't care. I gotta do something. I would have already gotten far if your group didn't cock-block me last week!"

"Dude, I know. You saw how I was standing back? I didn't agree with that at all. Oh, by the way, watch out for John, bro. Something ain't right. He has it in for you."

I had to warn him. Something *wasn't* right. John is not normally *this* nice. I know these guys. I play along with them, but something's definitely brewing.

"Thanks my friend, I knew you weren't like that. I could tell. Haha, no worries. I got my game already setup. I can't wait till Sunday."

"Yeah, so that speech! I'm psyched too honestly. Brother, if you can give me points to improve my lot as well? Shoots, I would be happy."

Mark looked at me. At the time, I didn't realize why he did, but looking back, I understood.

"Why don't I give you a preview now?"

"Really? You would share some of the stuff now? I thought you couldn't share..."

"Nah, for you my friend, I will. Matter of fact, you're a good guy, so instead of my speech, I will give you everything I know. Not a lot of dudes would have let me do my thing on Wednesday with Alice. You have integrity, and you understand the code. I realized then, that you weren't like the rest of the guys here."

Mark then got up, went to his room, and brought out a small notebook. It had lots of notes and pointers about all sorts of stuff. The stock market, clothes buying techniques and fittings, how to market to financial managers and investors, all of it.

I asked him where he got the book from, or if he wrote it.

"It's a secret, my friend. I got it from someone, now, I'm giving it to you."

"Seriously? I mean, I can't take this. This is your work."

"No, you can have it. I already know and practice everything in that book. Plus I have essentially memorized all of it. It's time to pass it on. Use it wisely my friend."

My man, Mark. I didn't realize it yet, but he had given me an amazing gift. All for free. All because I didn't judge him as soon as he got here.

We then drank a few beers and we started watching a game. During breaks, he explained how to use the book, and to omit certain parts if you're married, etc.

I spent about three hours over at his house. That was a good afternoon.

About three quarters through the game, I looked at my watch and my wife was almost home, so I told Mark I had to go.

Mark got up, shook my hand, and told me to always, always keep the book hidden, even from my wife. The book contained contact numbers to authentic rich people and business managers I could contact for favors and advice should I need it.

I promised I would and got up to put on my shoes.

"You're a good guy, Mark, damn, I wish I met you years ago."

"You're a good guy too Michael. I'm glad I met you. I will see you, ok?"

"You got it, brother. Talk this weekend. Oh, by the way, enjoy Alice, bro. I know it ain't right, but damn. Enjoy yourself, brother!"

Mark laughed.

"I will my friend, I will."

* * * * *

The weekend came, and it was nice. The weather was warm and comfortable, and people were outside chatting and talking about Sunday night's speech. It was still late morning, and Mark was home getting ready for the night and appeared like he was busy with boxes and other stuff. I suppose he was looking for old notes. Towards the afternoon, my wife was asking about cooking something to bring. She wanted to know what we should bring, and I told her to just bake a few cakes, nothing special, as I'm sure John probably got most of the food ready. So my wife baked three cakes. Two chocolate and one vanilla. Towards the late afternoon, I drove to the venue to take the cakes early before the event started, so that when we were walking in later that night, we wouldn't be lugging in cakes in our arms.

When I got to the venue, lo and behold, Alice was there, sitting in the front, chatting away with my man, Mark. I saw them and waved hello, but didn't go close, and set the cakes down on the large table with the rest of the food, then waved goodbye and left. I spotted what Alice was wearing before I walked out. She was wearing a short black dress, with a small bow at the back, and she had her makeup on and her signature fashionable glasses. Hair was done beautifully. Mark was wearing a shirt and tie, but no blazer on, but the shirt looked crisp and neat. I wondered what they were talking about, but I knew I couldn't stay. In any case, I could always ask Mark later. We were secret friends now anyway.

When I got home, I took my shower and got ready. It was starting to get dark, and people were all getting ready to leave to go to the venue. As we all left, I saw Tom heading out with his wife as well and waved to him. He drove in front of me, heading in the direction of the venue.

I and my wife jumped in the car, and as we drove down the street, my wife mentioned that she was a little thirsty and forgot to drink some water. She sometimes coughs if her throat gets dry. We could eat at the venue, but it would be an hour before the first break, so I didn't want her to be thirsty until then.

I stopped at a drive-through close by and picked up a bottle of water. As I was driving out towards the street, I saw what looked like Mark's brown BMW drive by, headed back in the direction of the neighborhood. It was so unmistakable that I recognized it. He had tinted windows, so I couldn't see anyone inside, but I knew it was his car.

I didn't think much of it, as I figured if anything, he probably forgot a last-minute thing, and ran home really quick to grab it.

When I got to the venue, I parked and went inside. Everyone was nicely dressed and people were standing around, chatting. I let my wife go mingle with some of the ladies, and met up with some of the guys in our group. John was there, smiling. He was a corny ass dude. He wore a damn bowtie. I mean, really? I tell you. Nothing wrong with a bowtie, but John did *not* wear it well. If anyone was alive that should not wear a bowtie, it was this guy.

"You fellas ready?" I asked.

"Yes sir," said Tom, smiling cheek to cheek as well.

I think John and Tom had gotten together and was planning something that me and even the rest of the guys in the group did not know about. These guys were snakes, man. I mean, you already planned to embarrass the guy. You even planned to boo him, even if things went well. What now? What were you two snakes planning to do now? I thought back to that Friday afternoon when Mark told me that he saw that I wasn't like the other guys. He was right. I was *not* like these guys. Only looking to bring a guy down. Just because you are jealous. Jealous of what? His clothes? He bought them. He didn't steal them. However he earned his money, he paid for his nice things. Were they so jealous because he was handsome? He was born that way. You can't choose how you look or arrange your DNA. Geez. I liked and admired Mark. I admire people who I think are better than me. I don't hate on them. These guys? They were nothing but haters.

I secretly wished at that moment, that Mark would destroy these hecklers when they tried to heckle him while he was on stage. Many a comedian has successfully done it. No reason why Mark couldn't turn on them and make them a damn example. *I hoped that he would.* These idiots needed to be taught a lesson.

It was getting closer to the time for the event to start, so John got on the mic, and asked everyone to start getting seated. The president of the homeowner's association was in attendance, sitting just behind our table, but his wife, Alice, wasn't present. I turned around and asked the president if Alice was coming.

"Yeah. She needed to run home to pick up something. She said it would only be fifteen minutes, but it's been about ten minutes now."

"Oh ok, enjoy the speech, sir," I said and turned around.

As John stood on the mic, he said he would spend just a few moments greeting everyone and warming up the crowd for Mark. He spoke for about five minutes and made some light, corny jokes. After the first five minutes, the president began to look around, as Alice was nowhere in sight. He didn't move, however, for another ten more minutes.

After John was finished up his opening, he introduced Mark as the *"Amazing Self-Help Guru"* and called on Mark to come up whenever he was ready. The crowd applauded and the lights dimmed.

As the lights were dimming, the president got up, touched me on the shoulder and whispered that he would go check on Alice, as she should have been back by now, and walked out.

I found that to be strange as well, as they lived not even two miles away. She should have *definitely* been back by now.

As the lights went to black, Mark did not immediately come to the stage.

John called for him again, but he didn't come out from behind the back as planned.

My wife looked at me, and whispered, *"Didn't you mention you saw Mark's car driving back home?"*

I looked at her and as I was about to answer, it came to me. My eyes lit up big. It *freaking* came to me.

I touched my wife on the hand and shook my head and motioned her to be quiet and to not say a word. She listened and leaned back in her seat and picked up her small water bottle and took a sip and smiled.

She figured it out. My wife was smart too.

After another five minutes, people began to whisper and get restless. I told my wife to stay put and went up to John and asked him what was happening.

"I don't know Michael. Mark didn't come in, and he's not answering his phone."

"Where is that guy?" Tom asked.

"I don't know, I thought he was here?" I answered, knowing full well he wasn't.

"Well, he better show up soon. People are getting restless."

I was dying in my heart. Everyone was waiting at the venue, but I was pretty sure I knew exactly where Mark and dear Ms. Alice was, and what they were doing. I wanted to bust out in laughter so bad! But I held my peace.

"Yeah me too. I want to hear him talk." I said.

One of the other guys said he was probably running late. I laughed in my mind again. Running late huh? That's what you think he was doing? Running late? You mean *"running late"* in bed with another man's wife! Haha! Again, sorry Mr. HOA President. Sorry. You are a good guy. You are the only guy I feel bad for right now. Your wife is sadly *"running late"* with my man, Mark.

Then I realized it. The president had gone to check on her. He had headed home.

"Oh shit!" I said to myself. Mark was gonna get caught!

* * * * *

After another ten minutes, I volunteered to go and check on Mark myself. Tom and John were furious. They said I needed to find him and get him here *asap*, and ask him if he somehow forgot what day the engagement was for. I was going to leave my wife there at the event, but she knew what was happening, and was not gonna let me go by myself. She said I was crazy if I thought she was gonna miss this. I let her come, and we got to our car and drove home.

Once we got to the neighborhood, we noticed that all the lights were on at the President's house. There was loud screaming, and you could hear the sound of broken glass shattering. The president was furiously screaming. I immediately stopped the car and ran towards the house, when my wife called me back and told me that I really shouldn't get involved. She knew what was happening, and wanted me to stay out of it. I told her I heard broken glass and wanted to make sure everything was ok.

She told me I still shouldn't go, as this was not my business. She said that she knows the President was a smart guy and he knew better than to hurt her and that if we felt that it was getting dangerous, we should call the police to intervene instead since it was a domestic issue.

She was right. It wasn't gonna be wise for me to show up. I didn't want it to look as if I knew about it, or if I told on Mark or anything, as I had no idea they were planning their tryst. Well, I did have a feeling, but I had nothing to do with it of course.

As I sat back in my car, I heard another glass break on the floor and I heard more yelling and screaming. I was about to take out my phone when

I heard an elderly neighbor shout that she was calling the police.

As the police showed up, we stayed parked a fair distance away and watched as the president came out, explained what had happened, and stood aside. Then Alice came out and spoke to the police. Mark was nowhere to be seen. He most likely ran away upon their discovery in bed by the president. The president would not have been able to physically hold down Mark anyway, so he was probably able to get on his clothes, and run out of the house.

It appeared that Alice told the police that they had a fight that got out of hand and that she wasn't pressing charges, but asked the police to make the president sleep in a hotel just for one night to calm down, then he could come back the next morning.

The president agreed to this and said he would find a hotel for the night, and they would talk in the morning about what happened. He then got in his car, and drove off, in the direction of the venue.

Of course, to let everyone know what had transpired.

Mark was *busted.*

We didn't even bother going back to the event. We went home and talked close to 2 am, discussing what happened, and if I knew any of this was happening before. I didn't want my wife to know, so I told her I saw them talking once, but I didn't think anything of it. I had to lie. You see, my wife would get her info from me, as all the other wives do, then go spread and disseminate that info amongst the other women. I couldn't let such sensitive info get out there. I know what Mark did was wrong, but this was between two consenting adults. Alice was *just* as wrong as him, even more so. She was married. Mark was not. They both wanted to do it. I would not betray one party like that. Besides, my wife was right, I should stay out of it.

We finally fell asleep, close to 2:30 am.

That morning, I got up to take a jog again. I didn't really have to, but I was curious about the president and Alice, and also about Mark. Was he home? Did he also go to a hotel that night to get away from the obvious heat he would have to face the next day?

As I jogged past Mark's house, I noticed the windows were clear see-through, and the blinds were removed.

I jogged closer and slowed down to take a peek, his garage was closed with no car inside, and the windows allowed me to peer through.

Mark's house was empty! All the furniture and art were mostly gone, and the living room looked like an empty showroom. I wondered how anyone could have moved their things so quickly and wondered if Mark had put his stuff in storage or something to avoid people maybe breaking in and breaking his expensive stuff when he wasn't home since people would be angry with him. I still didn't realize the truth. Not yet.

A car pulled up just then. A lady came out and walked up to the door and opened it. I was pretend-jogging across the street and ran over as soon as I saw her open the door. I called her and asked her if she knew Mark.

"Mark? Sure, I know him, why?"

"Oh, I just wanted to see if he was ok. I know he had a rough night last night."

"Oh, he did? I just saw him a few moments ago, he gave me back the keys. He was smiling and thanked me for all my help in finding him this place to use."

"Huh? He gave you back the keys and moved out? Is he selling this place? Wow!"

"Selling? No, Mark doesn't own this place. I rented him the place for a few weeks, while he found another place to live. I initially put up the "for sale" sign for a few hours one day a few months ago, but I decided to take it down just so people wouldn't keep asking me about it, and so the neighborhood would be comfortable, but this place has always been up for sale for a couple of months now."

"What? Really?" I was shocked.

"Yes. Do you know if someone is interested?" She answered.

That's when it finally and sincerely hit me. I laughed out loud for like thirty seconds. The poor lady thought I was crazy, but she started laughing at me too. You know how when you laugh at something and people see you, and start laughing at you, because you look so funny laughing, and they start laughing with you? That's what happened.

I finally understood it. Mark was, as I always thought, a true genius. We weren't ready for him. *No one was.*

Mark was *not* a successful, rich man. Mark was *not* a grand character or adviser to billionaires. Mark was *not* a *Self-Help Guru.*

Mark was, for all intents and purposes, a *conman.*

That day, I smiled while at work and all that afternoon. I was not mad. Not at all. Not one bit. Mark had gotten here, laid on the charm, conned the whole lot of us, and bust out the joint. All with a cool ten grand. Woo! I loved it. I really did. Best of all? Johnny-boy had put up the majority of the money for the event! He lost the most! Haha! I lost maybe what? $160? That was super minor to me anyway.

I called my wife at work and told her the story. I couldn't hide this fact, because eventually, it would come out anyway. She laughed and laughed over the phone. It was very amusing to her. She asked me how much we lost. I told her just $160. She was dying. I told her John lost the most. She was so amused!

As I was driving home, I then remembered the book.

Yes, The Book!

Mark had given me his treasure. I got home and went to the secret place I hid it in the garage amongst my tools, where I know my wife would never go and look through, and there it was. The book containing all of Mark's secret info. I flipped through it and then, only then, realized that it contained a full network of "business" men. That is, a book of rich conmen, who all worked by helping each other to attain, succeed, and learn the ropes of the conman world.

Upon realizing what the book actually contained, I told myself that I would never use it, but that I would keep it. I would read it, and learn the game. I vowed never to use it to harm my wife, and would only use some of the tips to be successful.

At the back of the book, there was a number for a few guys, and a number with the initials M.R. was written next to it. I thought I would take the chance.

I called the number with my cell phone. No one answered, but I left a quick message saying that it was Michael, and I was looking for Mark, and that I finally got what he meant, and that it was brilliant, and that I wished him good luck. That's all I said.

Later that night, while in bed, my phone got a text from a generic number. I knew who it was.

It said:

"Hey, my friend. I'm doing well, sorry I couldn't say goodbye, but I think you now know why. I was never gonna give that speech. Take care of yourself, read that book I gave you, keep it safe, and live a good life. Oh, and don't tell anyone, but I had a good time with A. Glad I got the chance, even if it was just once. She's a freak! Lol! Tell her I'm sorry if her marriage doesn't work out, but such is life. Be well my friend, and I hope we meet again one day. Use the book well. Take care, M."

I read it once, then read it again the second time. I was smiling ear to ear. My wife asked me what I was reading that was so funny. I told her I just got a text from a friend. She trusted me, almost as if she knew it was from Mark. She turned around, turned off the lights, and went to sleep.

I looked at the phone and thought back to all that had happened in the last few weeks. It was one hell of a ride! I never encountered a full-on, live, *professional* conman like that. That's the stuff of movies and tv shows. The dedication and training! People underestimate the skill to keep an act like that up.

I read the text message one last time, then held up the phone and erased the message. I then plugged my phone in the charger, and turned towards my wife, spooned her and hugged her close, kissed the back of her head, and drifted off to sleep.

The Decision

"We sometimes look for grand experiences our happiness to shape, we even seek to fly, without a superhero's cape. When we realize the truth, and miss our one true calling, it's essentially too late, for we're already falling."

It was a sunny afternoon. As Nigel looked up at the sky, he smiled as he walked towards the plane at the airport with excitement. The appointment had been booked earlier that week, as he had made up his mind. He would do it. He would do something that he was terrified to do. He would conquer his fears. He would tame his anxieties. He would smash away all his regrets. He would venture to confront all his demons, brush them all aside, and jump...

* * * * *

Nigel was a happy kid. Some might even say, a bit too happy. The boy seemed to drip glee and smiles. He was always smiling. He often played with his friends, and very few things could get him down. Nigel was always content and always happy to show his happiness to others. He had loving parents, and he never got into any trouble. As he grew up, however, this began to change. Life got in the way. Life did what it does best; that is, it shows you exactly how *unhappy* this world *really* is.

Nigel experienced his first death, as he watched Police shoot and kill a man who lived in his building on suspicion of drugs and other miscellaneous crimes. The man was not a saint, he had done bad things. But Nigel always remembered the guy as a nice guy to all the children on the block. In the summer, he would give a lot of the children quarters and sometimes a whole dollar, to go buy an icee for themselves when they were coming home from playing in the park. He would always ask the kids how they were doing, and if they were doing their homework. To Nigel, he was the nicest man he had ever met, besides his own father.

Yet the man had committed crimes and sold drugs. Nigel watched, along with the whole building, as he saw the man gunned down by police, believing him to have a weapon, when in fact, it was his cellphone. This had happened numerous times to people, and Nigel wondered why it kept happening.

Nigel also experienced real sadness, when he watched, as his grandmother suffered in the hospital, bedridden with Cancer at the young age of 67. She had his mother in her early twenties, and was still relatively young herself, despite now having grandkids. He watched as his grandmother suffered in pain and cried. She eventually passed. As a boy, transitioning to a man, he began to realize quickly, that life was not all happiness.

As such, Nigel lost the happiness of his youth.

As a grown man now 21, he had already become jaded. Jaded and confused at a world that took so much, and gave back so little. He was aware that happiness and good were still there, but that it was almost always overshadowed by the bad things that happened. There was always plenty of time to spend on bad things, but the good times passed quickly and were fleeting. He realized this as a man, now entering the full tenets of adulthood.

* * * * *

Nigel had gotten a girlfriend. She was very sweet to him most of the time and often teased him about life and other miscellaneous things. It never bothered him, and they had a good, trusting relationship.

One day, as Nigel was walking with his girl, he stopped to listen to two guys as they had a conversation near their building. The men were talking about life, and how time was so short, and that before you die, you should do something spectacular, so that you live with no regrets. This jolted something in Nigel, for he had become jaded and only saw the world as one big giant regret. Regret for past mistakes. Regret for not spending enough time with his grandmother in her later years before her death. Regret for not doing the things that made him happy. Regret from hiding away from his fears, and not embracing and conquering them.

But how could a young man be so regretful? Surely his life was just beginning, and he had time to accomplish all the things he wanted to do. Perhaps he was too hard on himself…

"Life is short…" One of the men said again. *"you gotta live life while you can."*

This rung true to Nigel, who at this point in his life, has experienced two vivid deaths. One of the man who once lived in their building, and the other of his grandmother, who passed away from cancer. Nigel knew quite well, how short life could be, and that as a man, he could die at any moment. This was the deciding factor. This is what ultimately led to Nigel's fateful decision.

Nigel was scared of heights. He always was, even as a little boy. He would take great pains to avoid getting to the top of little walls and never climbed trees as a kid. He would stand on the ground, content, and happy to watch the other boys, as they climbed and held onto branches, but he himself never did so, and stayed safe on the ground, and played amongst the boys.

Nigel, now with his mind made up, turned and looked at his girlfriend. He would do something; something to embrace his fears and conquer them; something to throw his regrets to the wind. Something that would make him truly happy. Something to live *spectacularly*.

Nigel asked his girlfriend what the most spectacular and exciting thing she had ever done was.

"I don't know babe. I rode a roller coaster when I was fifteen for the first time. That was probably the most scared and excited I have ever been. Why do you ask, babe?"

"Because I want to do something. Something big."

"Like what? Do you wanna do the Superman ride at Six flags, or…?"

"No, no. I want to do something that embraces my fears and regrets."

"Regrets? What regrets babe?"

"I regret not doing the things that make life exciting and enjoyable. I want to change that. I want to embrace my fears. I want to conquer them before I die."

"Ok, but what do you wanna do? I know you don't like Spiders or Snakes. I know you also don't like heights. Do you wanna go to the zoo next week and see some snakes and some big tarantula spiders? Oooo!" His girlfriend teased.

"No, no snakes babe. Something else."

"What then? You wanna conquer your fear of heights? Wanna go to New York City and go to the top of the Empire

State Building and look down? That would freak you out babe!"

Nigel looked at his girlfriend. She had given him an idea. This idea would prove to be the most important idea he had ever made, and although he didn't realize it back then, he knew it was something he wanted to do, come what may.

"You know what, I'm gonna jump."

"Jump?" His girlfriend asked. *"Like Bungee jump? You wanna go bungee jumping?"*

"No. Not bungee jumping."

His girlfriend thought for a moment.

"You wanna go base jumping? Babe! That's kinda dangerous!"

"No. Not base jumping. As a matter of fact, I wanna do something even better. Even bigger. More spectacular. I want to jump, but not off a base or cliff, but out of a plane."

"You wanna jump out of a plane?" His girlfriend repeated, somewhat shocked.

"Yes babe, I wanna jump out of a plane. I want to fall through the sky…"

He looked at his girlfriend and smiled.

"I want to go skydiving."

* * * * *

Nigel called a skydiving service close to where they lived. To his luck, there was a skydiving place in New Jersey, which was nearby, so Nigel decided to do the jump with them. The appointment was setup fast, and the service could fit him in the following week, that Sunday afternoon, as the weather would be favorable, and the wind speeds would be mild, making the jump less turbulent for first-time jumpers.

As he made preparations for the jump and followed the instructions the skydiving service gave him, his girlfriend, quite unhappy at Nigel's new-found bird-like confidence, tried to convince him not to go.

"Let's think this through Nigel. I'm not saying don't do it, but I feel like you are doing it for the wrong reasons."

"Why would you think that?" Nigel asked.

"Because you want to conquer your fear of heights. So why not go to the building roof and look down or something, then come back downstairs. Why do you have to jump from a plane?"

"I could do that, but that won't prove anything to me. I need to do the most extreme form of height. I need to prove to myself that I did the ultimate thing a human can do in terms of heights. Then, only then, will I feel like I've conquered my fear. Only then can I be happy with me"

"But there are other ways, Nigel..."

"Maybe, but this is what I want to do. I need your support babe. I know you don't like this, but I have to do it. It's very safe. Plus, I won't be jumping alone. The skydiving service told me that a professional person is strapped to me, since this is my first time, and essentially, they do everything. I just have to sit back, follow all instructions, and just have the experience."

"But there are other ways to be happy. Didn't you tell me that one day you wanted to write a book? It could even be about encouraging people to safely overcome their fears without doing the thing that they fear. That would make a lot of sense actually..."

"That won't be enough for me, babe."

"And skydiving would be enough for you Nigel? Won't you become, like, some kind of addicted skydiving freak, hooked on the adrenalin and doing it almost every day until something happens to you? I don't like this. Maybe you shouldn't..."

"Babe, stop. I have no intentions to keep doing that. I just need to do this one time to prove to myself that I confronted and embraced my fears, and I didn't let it stop me. I'm pretty sure when I get back home, that I will still be afraid of heights, you know. But at least, I embraced it and didn't let it define me. That's living with no regrets."

"Nigel, I know I can't stop you, but please, please be safe."

"Of course I will babe. I don't want to die…"

"Don't even say that. Just be safe, follow all instructions, and come back in one piece ok?"

"I will babe. I will."

Nigel spent the next few days reading all the material he got from the skydiving service and tried his best to memorize concepts from the internet in what to do in case there is any trouble. He slept nervously, but expectantly the night before the jump.

That next morning, he woke up, had breakfast with his family, and spent the remainder of the morning with his girlfriend, and even made her cry by joking that she should prepare a will on her phone. He then apologized for teasing her so seriously, and gave her a ring he had bought for her with her birthday month gemstone, a blue topaz, and promised to be safe and come back home that same afternoon, no matter what.

* * * * *

As Nigel arrived at the skydiving field, he looked up at the sky. The weather was warm and still. The wind slightly blew, but the breeze was gentle and cool. Birds were seen flying high up in the sky and they too seemed to be calm. They were free to soar as high as they wanted. They didn't need to take all these protective precautions. They could fly as high or as low as they liked. Birds were the lucky ones, he thought, as he walked towards the hangar where he would meet the skydiving instructor and go through all the preparations before jumping.

Nigel listened carefully to the instructor, as he explained that they would be going up to around 14,000 feet, but since this was the first time Nigel had jumped, the instructor explained that they would go an extra 500 feet, to allow for small adjustments and a few more seconds to react to any form of disturbance or danger. Nigel thanked the instructor and was glad that he was considering everything for his safety, and promised he would do everything as instructed.

A few more minutes passed, and Nigel and the skydiving instructor walked out to the waiting plane and climbed on board. Nigel did not hesitate. The instructor asked him if he needed to do anything before jumping. Nigel replied that he was ok, and was ready. The plane took off.

As they climbed in the air, Nigel looked out the window. He watched, as the sun was shining brightly in the upper part of the west, as it was beginning its descent towards sunset. He watched as the green parts of the land grew farther and farther away, becoming like little patches of green and brown smudges. He thought about everything he had done so far in life. He was proud of himself. He was proud that he was doing something to embrace his fears. He was proud that he chose to be someone who wanted to live without regrets. Yes, he would live, all without having any regrets.

As the plane neared its cruising height for them to jump, the instructor went over again with Nigel, all instructions and what to do. He ensured Nigel understood everything and confirmed that Nigel did not have to do anything. His part would come in later, as they neared the ground, as he was supposed to tuck his feet under him as they were about to land with the parachute to avoid injuring his leg, but would be fully coached by the instructor the whole way through. He double and triple checked all the landing gear, and strapped Nigel in front of him and tugged as hard as he could on the straps and clasps, to ensure they were locked into place and secure.

Now, the moment had come. The door of the plan was opened, and Nigel and the instructor were strapped in, and ready to take the plunge. The instructor asked if Nigel wanted to go on a three-count or to just close his eyes and let him decide. Nigel opted for the three count. They would both jump, together. This, he thought, was the ultimate proof that he did it, of his own volition.

One...Nigel stood at the door and looked down. They were so high, and all he could see was clear, open air. Nigel took a quick, deep breath. *Two*...Nigel held onto the instructor and steadied his heart. He said a silent prayer to God for safety, and closed his eyes. *Three*...no turning back now...

At three, they both, with one motion, jumped out of the cruising plane.

As Nigel felt himself fall out of solid ground into the open air, his heart jumped. He instantly felt the sensation of gravity enacting its part of the bargain with fourth-dimensional beings. He felt, as it began to do its job as it always had done, since the creation of the earth. It began to pull him and the instructor down. Down with the sensation of air pushing against your face, the sensation of realizing that gravity was an immutable law, and it didn't give a damn if you wanted to take part in that realization or not.

He felt the *sensation* of falling.

Nigel felt a rush of adrenaline all over his body. They were falling. So very fast. He had looked at videos of people doing it, and it seemed as if the people were floating, and surely, they were floating up there, having all that fun, twisting, flipping and becoming professional gymnasts. He closed his eyes and imagined himself doing all those things in the air as well. Perhaps the instructor would flip them over in the air...

The instructor tapped Nigel on the shoulder. Nigel looked at him from the side. He saw the instructor make a "thumbs up" sign with his left hand. Nigel shook his head in acknowledgment. The instructor tapped him on the opposite shoulder again, confirming that all was well.

They had now fallen the first 500 feet. 14,000 left to go.

* * * * *

As they fell past another 500 feet, Nigel smiled. He could feel the wind on his cheeks. It was hard, but not limiting. He could still move his mouth and turn his face. He looked over at the horizon and saw the sun, still shining as brightly as it was, watching their descent, sending just a little bit of sunshine their way, as if to cheer them on. Nigel felt it and became happy. He opened his mouth and let out a long scream. It was a scream of freedom. Sure, the jump was exhilarating, but Nigel screamed because he was so very proud of himself. He had taken the chance and did something truly spectacular. He felt invincible and began waving his arms in the air, batting it against the wind. He opened his palms and let the air beat it, rushing past them as the air molecules bumped into the skin on his palms and said hello, then rushed away, as others stopped by, greeted his hand, and flew away, probably never to interact with his skin again.

As Nigel waved his arms in the air, he felt his belt strap for his pants slip a little to the left, settling on top of his belt, strapping himself to the instructor. Nigel ignored it, but it became slightly uncomfortable, so he put his left hand to his chest, and used his right hand to adjust the belt buckle. He adjusted it in one quick motion, and let his arms out again.

The instructor noticed it and tapped him on his left shoulder. This time Nigel made a "thumbs up" sign with his arms to let him know he was ok. The instructor tapped him on the right shoulder in confirmation.

As they fell past another 1000 feet, Nigel shouted and looked around as they fell. "Whoo! This is amazing!" He shouted. He was now in the zone. Nigel was in the middle of it all, experiencing the sheer excitement of falling to the earth, and nothing could encroach on this feeling. He screamed out more and more, and the instructor even joined in with his enthusiasm, and shouted "whoo-hoo!" as well, as Nigel was having the time of his life.

They had now fallen about 2,000 feet. 12,500 left to go.

* * * * *

They fell past the 11,000-foot mark, and the instructor tapped Nigel, as now, they were nearing terminal velocity. The ground would start to come quicker and quicker towards them, and they needed to prepare for landing procedures soon. Nigel shouted one more time, then put his arms to his chest, confirming that he was ready to follow all instructions. As the instructor tugged on a few key wires, Nigel felt it. It was slight, but he felt his position, relative to the instructor, shift only slightly. He didn't think of it, as the instructor had strapped him in very well. The instructor was just making sure he had access to the wires and handles he would need for the parachute, and was making sure everything was ready. He was very safe and skilled. As he pulled on the final strap, the one across Nigel's waist, he felt a little more give, and then, to the instructor's horror, a release.

This is when things went wrong.

As Nigel felt the strap move past him, he instantly felt the tight strap that was securing him to the instructor loosen and felt his weight give forward, separating him a few inches from the safety of the instructor.

Nigel began to slip backward, towards the instructor's feet.

They had now fallen 5,000 feet. 9,500 feet left to go.

The instructor, instantly realizing something had gone wrong, grabbed onto Nigel with his left hand and held his waist tightly. Nigel could feel that this was not normal and began to shift his weight forward, attempting to correct the distance they once had whilst strapped close together. This did not help things, and Nigel drifted further back. The instructor, now keenly aware of the danger, tapped Nigel with the code to remain still. He didn't want Nigel to move and began to take measures to correct the position and keep Nigel from slipping further back. Nigel began to feel scared but trusted in the instructor to sort things out and keep them both safe.

The instructor was very experienced and knew what to do. He held onto Nigel with one arm, then used the other arm to secure the strap and attempt to place it back around Nigel's waist. Nigel saw that and tried to help the instructor, by using his left hand to grab the strap and assist with returning the strap in place. However, this was a mistake. Nigel had moved his arm, and this single action had put extra pressure on the instructor's arm, holding him in place as they were falling and the wind was rushing past them, interacting with their arms as they fell.

Nigel began to slip even further back, at the full extension of the instructor's arm.

Nigel began to panic. He started flailing his arms and legs. The instructor, trying to keep Nigel calm, began to tap quickly on his shoulders. Sadly, this no longer worked. Nigel began grasping at anything that he could. He started pulling on his straps and other various safety mechanisms, in an attempt to hold on. The instructor, using all his strength, was holding onto Nigel's clothes, trying to tap on him and shout at him to tell him to calm down, but his arms began to cramp and give way.

As Nigel felt the instructor's grip loosen, he thought he heard the instructor say, "Oh, God!" as Nigel slipped completely backward, and out of the straps keeping him and the instructor together.

Nigel was now falling, completely separated from the instructor, without a parachute, falling essentially, to his demise.

You see, only slightly earlier, unbeknownst to Nigel and the instructor, Nigel had adjusted what he *thought* was his pants belt. Only it wasn't his belt he wore on his pants. He had instead, loosened and almost released the safety strap that was around his waist and ran under his groin. This was also the strap that connected his parachute to him. This was not the instructor's fault. It was Nigel's. In his excitement, Nigel had made a grave mistake and doomed himself.

They had now fallen 7,500 feet, with 7,000 feet left to go.

As Nigel felt himself slip out of his harness, he closed his eyes for what felt like five seconds. Time seemed to slow down. In reality, he had only blinked. Upon opening his eyes, he looked up, as he saw the instructor falling away from him, as he began to be tossed in every direction. He was on his back, then flipped upside down, then back on his chest, then falling with his foot in the air. Nigel began to scream. He instantly felt like he wanted to pass out. He felt nauseous and began to vomit. Then, just as he coughed on the vomit leaving his throat, he passed out.

* * * * *

As Nigel got to the tenth grade, he had begun to take his first high school classes in Physics. The teacher was very knowledgeable but practical and taught the students the fundamentals of the natural law in a simple, but fun way.

Distance: The space between two objects or subjects.

Said the professor to the boys:

"Your girlfriend is at the other end of the room, and you wanna kiss her. You are in the hallway outside the class. The space between you and your girlfriend is the distance between you."

The boys understood that quickly and shook their heads in acknowledgment. The girls also understood, but just laughed at the silly boys.

Speed: How fast you are going in a set distance from point A to B, relative to people watching you.

"If two cars are driving," said the knowledgeable Professor, *"and one is going at 10mph, and the other is driving at 20mph, then the 10mph and 20mph numbers themselves are the speed. It is measured by our set defined rules for miles per hour."*

The students thought the professor was a cool guy, as he was young, hip, and explained difficult concepts to them in a simple way.

Acceleration: "If a car is driving at 20mph, and you pushed the gas pedal, and the car's engine does more work and makes the car go faster to 40mph, the car accelerated from 20mph to 40mph, or in other words, it increased its speed within a set amount of time, in a given distance."

Nigel, a lowkey jokester in school, raised his hand. He had a question.

"So if one of the girls wanted to hug me, and I'm just walking towards them, and then she shouts that she wants to make out with me, and I start running fast towards her, then I accelerated myself to get to her faster, right?"

The professor was quite amused with Nigel's way of putting it but confirmed that yes, he would have accelerated his speed towards this *poor, unfortunate girl.* The class laughed.

Velocity: "The speed of something headed in a given or specific direction."

The professor said that sometimes this was mistaken for speed itself, and sometimes for acceleration as well.

Said the professor: *"Speed is just the measurement of how fast you are going in set defined rules or markers, like kilometers per hour or miles per hour. Velocity was the rate of speed you have in a specific direction towards an object."*

Piggybacking off of Nigel's earlier bad example, he explained that Velocity is the speed Nigel has as he is running *towards* the girl, but in *her direction.* Velocity then, *"is the measurement of speed in relation to the direction Nigel would be traveling."*

That is, he added, towards the *slap* the girl would give him when he arrived to try to kiss her. The class laughed again, and Nigel laughed too.

Terminal Velocity: The maximum speed an object can fall in a given direction, that is, in freefall towards the ground.

The professor asked the students to imagine that they were at the top of a skyscraper. Then he asked them to picture throwing a bowling ball over the side. He mentioned that no one should ever do that in real life, ever, but to just imagine it for the lesson. He stated that even though the ball was heavy and would fall fast, due to the pull of gravity from the earth, the maximum speed the bowling ball will fall is set at roughly 285mph. This has to do with the Bowling Ball's mass and density. *"For a human,"* the professor stated, *"the terminal velocity is much slower, at roughly 120mph, depending on your weight, mass, and the set density of the human body."*

These simple lessons, as the cool, hip professor taught it, were fun to learn, but Nigel, as he never imagined himself in his current position, completely forgot about all of it as he fell, reaching terminal velocity in the direction towards the ground and essentially, towards his death. In truth, it wasn't as if he could use any of these concepts of the natural law and save himself, for he only had a few moments left to live.

* * * * *

As Nigel fell, closer and closer to the Earth, he woke up. For one second, he didn't realize what was happening, but in the very next second, he became aware and began to flail his arms and legs again, panicked, as he fell. He began to look around for the instructor, to see if he was near to him, and thought for an instant, that the instructor would maybe do some sort of *James Bond* maneuver, and come flying in and grab him and deploy his parachute just in time. His mind began to race and think of all the scenarios of how it could happen. He imagined the instructor crashing into him and grabbing him, maybe slightly injuring his arm. He then instantly closed his eyes and stiffened his arm to brace for the impact. Such was the immense speed of thoughts that were going through Nigel's mind as he fell, panicked and alone.

In the next instant, as Nigel felt no such collision, he opened his eyes and looked in every direction he could see. He was still falling, all the while flailing, turning back and forth, head first, then arms, then back, then chest. He could see the instructor nowhere in sight. Finally, as the wind uprighted him to an orientation towards the sky, he saw what appeared to be a large open canopy, the parachute now open, and the instructor now floating, high above him.

The instructor, terrified but unable to save Nigel, fell for another thousand feet, but then as he neared the 5,000-foot threshold, he had no choice but to deploy his parachute.

Nigel had now fallen over 9000 feet, with roughly 5,000 feet left to go.

As Nigel turned around every which way in the air, he began to get nauseous and woozy again. This time, however, he did not vomit, and stayed awake, despite the sheer terror he was now experiencing.

He was falling. Falling like a downed bird, having lost his wings, that is, away from the skydiving instructor, who was his only lifeline to safety. Nigel continued screaming as he fell, his face, locked in terror, and at the same time shock, for he could not believe or understand what was happening to him.

Now, as Nigel looked, the ground appeared bigger and larger than a few seconds before, and he knew that soon, it would all be over. Nigel began to pray. He screamed out for God to save him. He screamed for help. He screamed for anyone, anything, a bird, or an eagle, anything to give him hope to latch onto.

Sadly, nothing came.

What could come in this situation anyway? No bird would have the strength to save him from falling. Time now seemed to slow down, and Nigel began to experience the true speed of time dilation for your thoughts, in such an extreme situation and began to think at a speed many, many times faster than normal human thought.

Nigel began to think about his life.

"Where did I go wrong?" He asked himself, partly praying to God as well.

"I'm only 21. I've never committed any crimes. O God! Why? What did I do wrong? Please! Someone help me!"

Nigel was rightly terrified. Terrified at what was happening to him. Mortified of dying at such a young age. He had made his mind to only live with no regrets, to not fear life, and to do something spectacular. This would surely make him happy. Was deciding to go skydiving so wrong? Who had he harmed? Why did this happen to him on his first and only attempt to skydive? Why him? All these questions passed through his mind in less than a nanosecond, as he plummeted, still over 4,000 feet in the air.

Suddenly, Nigel thought about his family. He began to instantly feel the pangs of regret and sadness for his parents and siblings. He instantly imagined the immense shock and pain they would experience when they found out he was dead. He knew there was no way he would survive the fall, and as such, he would die. He cried out again in anguish, for he envisioned the tears on his mother's face, as she would find out about the tragic accident.

His family would all be at the funeral. They would say nice, kind words about him. They would hold each other and cry. His friends would come and comfort his mother and his girlfriend, as they stood in black, staring and crying at his casket…

Oh no, his girlfriend.

Nigel began to recall all the happy times they had together. They had been together for a little over a year, but they had gone through a lot before this. She was there, even before they got together, as a friend, supporting him as he watched his grandmother pass. She was always there. Caring for him and teasing him. She would be devastated. Devastated to find out how he died.

Nigel felt deep emotions of regret, as he saw images of her, crying and sobbing at the news of his death. This was even doubly hurtful, for she didn't even want Nigel to go in the first place. He realized then that his *happiness* lay with her, for she truly loved him. Did he really need to do such an extravagant thing such as skydiving? Look what has now happened. He was falling to his death. Nigel began to pray in his mind, at rapid speed, for God to take care of her, and he asked God to make her forget about him, as he would be leaving her. He prayed for her good health, and her success, and asked for forgiveness for leaving her alone, all worried and anxious, never again being able to see him alive.

* * * * *

Nigel had now reached the threshold of 3,000 feet. He began to straighten up and strangely enough, settle in one position in the air. He was falling on his back, and he could now move his eyes quickly, right and left. He darted his eyes to the left, and saw the horizon, nearing his viewpoint, closer and closer. He darted his eyes to the right and saw the bright sun, still shining happily and comfortably, looking at him and smiling, as he torturously suffered and fell. He began to hate the sun. He began to hate everything.

Nigel began to feel emotions of sadness and anger. He began hating all the people who had did him wrong. All the people who didn't treat him right. He hated life itself and even became slightly glad that it was ending for him shortly because after all, life sucked hard. He had only wanted to do something to embrace his fears. Was this so wrong? He felt he had been given the wrong end of the stick, the *short straw*. He was young. Did he not deserve a chance at life like everyone else? Why did this have to happen to him? He was angry.

Looking towards the direction of his feet, he saw a plane, flying high above him as he fell. Flying, going about its merry way, not giving a damn that someone was falling, falling without anyone to help them.

He then thought about the terror of plane crash victims, who like him, were falling to their doom. He thought how terrified they all must have been. Then he thought about their families. He thought about how saddened their family members would have been to hear the soul-crushing news that their loved one perished in a plane crash.

He instantly felt sorry. Sorry that he was being selfish, and that many others had gone through the pain and anguish that his family will soon endure, and only wished that he had some way to comfort them in their trying hour.

Nigel then thought about the celebration of people who have previously passed. He thought back to happy times he spent with his grandmother and happy times with the man who always gave him a quarter to buy an icee from the corner store when he came home from playing in the park with his friends. He thought back to his loving parents and his friends. He thought back to how all the people in the building celebrated the man who was shot to death; how he was remembered and cherished, very fondly so, by all the people who knew him. This gave Nigel some comfort, as he knew that the people that mattered to him most, the one's closest to him, they would remember him and celebrate his life, his love, and his memory.

This seemed to calm Nigel down a little, and he began to stop screaming. Instead, he began to cry.

Nigel was now getting closer and closer to the ground. Trees and structures began visualizing themselves vividly, as he passed the 1,500-foot threshold. Not much time was left. The end would come soon, as Nigel began to think about what would happen to him as he died. Would he fall to the ground and die of the shock of all his broken bones? Or would he hit the ground and simply burst into pieces? Surely, he would be a wreck and a mess. He thought of the sight of himself, laying there, with his stupid, beady eyes open, dead as a doornail. He was crying in the air, crying knowing that he was going to die. Yet, as he pictured his silly face in the ground, bust into several thousand pieces, laying there like a sorry mangled mess, he did something strange.

He began to laugh.

He laughed as he felt that he would be found in a super embarrassing position. He laughed at the thought of some poor soul finding his body all maimed and deformed, like a stale old bag of bread, crusty and crushed. He laughed a little out loud, then stopped and began to smile. Smiling at his silly thoughts as he plummeted closer and closer to the Earth.

I mean, was this not an occasion to smile? Should he still be sad? In a few moments, it won't matter anyway. Nigel knew that he had to give it all up. The regret. The pain. The fear. The anger. Even the love. It all didn't matter to him personally now. He would die in the next few seconds, and leave everyone on this silly earth behind. This is what became funny to him.

He then thought about his mother again. This time, he thanked God in his heart for her, and even though she would be sad, he somehow knew that she would be ok. Same as with his girlfriend. He felt that she too, would one day move on, and forget about his silly, deformed, and stupid face.

His friends would laugh and remember him fondly. His teachers would remember him as a happy, joyful kid. This made Nigel happy.

"At the end of the day," he thought, "isn't that all a guy can ask for? To be remembered fondly? We all gotta die anyway. Might as well take my turn, now right?"

Indeed, Nigel had accepted what was going to happen to him. He was peaceful and calm. Now, no longer screaming, no longer panicked, he awaited his last few moments, calm and quiet, with a serene look on his face.

He was once again, proud of himself. Proud that he was calm. Proud of his bravery in facing his death calmly and even jokingly. Was this not even greater than facing all his fears at once? He had done something big indeed. He had embraced man's greatest fear, and after facing that fear, he laughed at it. Laughed at it with calmness and assurance.

Nigel had indeed done something special. Something big. Something *spectacular*. He was once again, happy. As a matter of fact, for those last remaining moments, he had regained the joy of his youth once more.

Nigel could see the tops of trees, coming closer and closer to him, now with what was only maybe three to five seconds left to him. He had now passed 500 feet. He quickly prayed once again, as he closed his eyes, and held onto his pants, hoping no one found him with his pants down. This was his final joke.

As Nigel landed, there was a slight poof as he burst into pieces on impact.

* * * * *

Later that afternoon, as the news reported that a man had died in a horrific skydiving accident, Nigel's girlfriend immediately knew it was him. His girlfriend began to laugh and cry. She had temporarily gone insane it appeared, for she understood the sheer irony and coincidence of the whole thing. Surely it was funny. The one time her boyfriend had chosen to do something different, was the one time he didn't come home.

She kept laughing and crying, as her phone rang. Ringing to tell her the news she already knew. It was Nigel's family. They had been informed and was calling to tell her that they had just found out the tragic news. She looked at the blue topaz ring, still in its box, that he had bought for her and given her that morning.

She picked it up off the table, with the phone ringing, and threw the box with the ring out the window.

She walked to her bedroom, still laughing and sobbing, and set her phone down on Nigel's side of the bed. She picked it up and looked at it to see who was calling. It was Nigel's mother.

She set it down on Nigel's pillow and watched, as it rang and rang.

She then said a prayer for him and hoped that whatever he experienced before his death, that it at least made him a little happy. She then kept looking at the phone as it continued to ring.

She didn't bother to answer it.

The Mocking of Bill Tackey, *The Mackey*

"If ever you feel someone is useless and not worth the trouble, come out of your small, self-aggrandizing bubble. For everyone has value, and a part to play, it may not be now, but you'll see it someday."

I n the hills up in the mountains, there was a small town nestled between a large surrounding mountain wall and a small lake, where a small population of people lived. Weather was fairly nice all year round, and the people were comfortable and mostly happy.

The town was poor, but everyone lived with each other and got along well. People desired more, but couldn't afford it, and were extreme penny pinchers when it came to buying anything modern or new. The surrounding towns were more developed and had access to many pieces of newer technology, making the people's lives who lived in the surrounding areas, much easier.

Being that the town was poor, they tried to make do with what they had, but oftentimes the people complained that the town was so much more behind when compared to surrounding towns. They simply wanted more.

The mayor, many years ago, after returning from a trip to a nearby town, found that the people there had all the luxuries of modern life and all manner of useful things provided by this modern era. All they could afford were basic things, such as regular, landline phones. They were mostly cut off from the rest of the world, with no proper internet access, whereby the surrounding towns had high-speed internet. The people in the town also could not afford heavy packages of such things like cable tv and often used basic antennas to pick up local, free programming. The wealthier among them used newer cell phones, but the majority of the people there mostly used landlines in their homes, as affording a monthly paid cell phone would be an extra bill they didn't want to pay for.

Mr. Tackey was a coal miner in the small town, who along with a group of men, would get up every day, and head for the mines in the mountains, putting in a solid day's work of back-breaking labor, then to return home to his wife and two kids, Mary and Bill. Most of the men in the town owned a small stake in the mine, and they regularly produced enough coal to keep the lights on, and for each man to sustain themselves, and their families. The township itself also owned a small share in the mine.

Mary, his daughter, was a sweet little child. She was so sweet in fact, that the townsfolk called her Mary Lamb. She always smiled at everyone and said the sweetest things. She was one year older than Bill. Everyone respected Mr. Tackey and his wife and loved Mary.

Bill, on the other hand, *not so much.*

Bill had been born with a degenerative disease and had also developed an extra chromosome, causing him to be born with Down's Syndrome. Bill was mischievous and destructive at times, but never harmful to anyone. The people mostly avoided letting their kids play with Bill, as he would sometimes destroy their toys, and seeing that they hated to spend an extra cent to buy a new one, Mr. Tackey would have to pay for it. Of course he did, as it was his son's fault when he destroyed other children's playthings. Due to this, Mr. Tackey mostly kept Bill with him and had him even come with him to the mines as the men on the surface kept an eye on him.

The townsfolk loved to give people nicknames and being that Mary Lamb already had a nickname, the men wanted to give Bill a nickname. Bill's father, Mr. Tackey, was a strong, respected gentleman in the town, and he was handsome. The men always teased him that he was a lover boy, even though he worked just as hard as them. They always felt he got one of the cutest girls in the town and said he was a lucky guy.

Bill, however, was mischievous but mostly harmless, so to tease Mr. Tackey, they started to refer to Bill as "*Bill Tackey, The Mackey*". This was amusing to his father, for *"Mackey"* meant that you would grow up to be manly, strong, prosperous, and virile, and so he hoped secretly, that one day, Bill would grow up and become functional enough to be the man he hoped he could be.

About ten years passed by, but Bill did not grow into the nickname the men gave him.

Now fourteen, Bill would go with his father every day to the coal mines, while Mary Lamb attended high school. He would try to watch the men and help out, but would often destroy sensitive equipment and cause damage to important things that the men needed, such as gauges and meters to safely gauge pressure and levels of poisonous gases in the air as they worked deep in the mine.

Bill was essentially not at all helpful to the men, and Mr. Tackey was soon forced to keep him outside the mine at the surface level and had him watch over non-important things.

Bill had a speech impediment, as it originated on account of his syndrome, but he would learn useful words as his mother taught him. He often used one word to describe things and most people understood him. When he wanted to go play, he would shout *"Play! Play!"* and his mother knew it meant he wanted to go play outside. When he was hungry, he would shout *"Belly!"* or *"Food!"* and his parents fed him.

Now a teenager, he would show more aggression and frustration when he didn't get his way, and oftentimes, only his father or mother could calm him down.

One time, when he was fourteen, Bill shoved Mary Lamb so hard, that she fell and bruised her elbows. It was the first time he had been violent with his sister, or anyone for that matter. The people did not like this, and even Bill's father, Mr. Tackey, a fair, but strict man, severely scolded and spanked him, and rightfully so, as he should never have shoved his sister like that. His mother agreed with his spanking and only asked her husband to ease a little after he gave Bill a few firm and stinging taps to his rear and hands as he cried and screamed from the pain. He was also warned by his mother that if he was violent with his sister again, she would not be so merciful to him, and would allow his father to spank him longer.

The reason Bill shoved Mary Lamb so hard was because, despite his learning disabilities, he had learned to become jealous of Mary, as he saw how nice she was treated, and how whenever he touched something, most people either pulled it away and out of his hand, or scolded and yelled at him to put it down or stop. He felt that she was getting all the good attention, and he had learned to distinguish the *bad attention.*

He became upset with Mary Lamb when she asked him not to play with one of their mother's wooden cooking utensils, as it could break. He had gotten it out of the kitchen and was playing with it outside. She took it out of his hand, as she and everyone always did, but since he had now developed feelings of jealousy, he expressed his frustration, screamed out, and shoved her as hard as he could. Mary Lamb hit the floor and scraped her elbows with white gashes to the flesh.

After his scolding by his parents, the people in the town also secretly chided and scolded Bill. When he walked with his father, they wouldn't shout at him, but they would ask him to be a nice boy and not to hit anyone. When his father wasn't around, they would chide him strongly, and tell him to keep away from their children and that he was a bad boy.

One day, as his mother walked to the store, she saw another lady yelling at Bill, and flew in a rage and demanded to know why the lady was yelling at Bill. Bill had snatched a toy from a younger child's hands and wanted it. Bill was now fourteen, and should not have wanted or needed a child's toy, but being that Bill had a developmental disability, he was essentially still closer to the child's age in many respects.

Bill's mother explained this to the lady and the lady deeply apologized but explained that when she saw what Bill did, it made her upset. Bill's mother asked the lady to have patience with Bill, as she should know that he was only large in size, but his mind was still mostly that of a child. The lady apologized once more and promised never to be so mean to him again. Bill's mother accepted the apology, and said that that would be the end of it; as she was a mother who was very understanding and fair, and knew that she might have felt the same way if someone else's child did that to her child. She then led Bill away.

* * * * *

One fateful day, as the men busily worked in the mine, Bill saw a large rat run into the entrance of the mine. He was sitting outside, picking up small pieces of wood and twigs when he saw it dash from behind a rock and head into the mine, seemingly escaping from Bill. Bill didn't like this and started running behind the terrified rat, chasing it deeper into the mine.

As the rat was faster than Bill could run, it got away, but not before Bill had crashed into a post on the left side of the wall. It shook but stood firm. One of the men who was working nearby shouted at Bill and told him he should leave and get outside and stop playing around in the mine or his father would be upset. Bill heard that and shouted back at the guy and said *"No!"* in frustration, then kicked the post again and walked back out of the mine, crying to himself that people always shouted at him.

After a few minutes of walking around outside, Bill suddenly heard what sounded like a bomb had gone off. He turned around and saw a huge waft of smoke rising from the entrance of the mine. He heard screams from the men as they struggled under the rubble.

The mine had collapsed.

Bill, not knowing what to do, ran towards the mine entrance, and began to move rocks, trying to get to the men inside. He was frustrated, but he knew that there was one person inside who was working deep in the mine: his father. He started calling out for his father and kept picking up large rocks to move them away.

People living nearby heard the explosion and ran to help. Women screamed out as they quickly realized the men were trapped and crushed, deep in the mine. They called for the authorities and fire trucks and people began to ask how it happened, as they hadn't had a mine collapse, not in over thirty years.

As the firemen and authorities worked tirelessly to dig through the rubble at the entrance, Bill stood there, silent. He was not fully aware of what happened but knew in some way, shape, or form that it was his fault. He ran away back home to his mother to tell her.

Later that day, as the news spread through the town, a single man was eventually pulled out of the rubble, badly hurt, but alive. He was close to suffocating and was deeply buried under a fairly large boulder, almost crushing him, but as he lay under another large wooden ledge, it held, saving his life, until the rescuers could get to him.

He had a broken wrist, a fractured hip bone with several broken ribs, and a large head wound that scraped across the side and back of his head. He was whisked away to the hospital. The authorities and rescuers kept working, well into the night and the next day, but still was unable to reach the men, trapped deep in the mine.

As the man was treated in the hospital for his injuries, he could talk, only barely, but it was enough to tell the police what happened.

Bill Tackey was responsible.

He was the man who had seen Bill chase a rat into the mine and watched as he bumped into one of the central posts, holding up a large boulder on the ceiling of the mine. The initial blow to the post shook the shaky post, but it did not give way. However, it shifted the weight of the boulder and loosened it. After he had shouted at Bill to get out of the mine, he then got upset and kicked it, loosening the boulder enough to eventually collapse.

The boulder didn't give way immediately. The man even walked over to the wooden post and inspected it after Bill walked out of the mine. As he was looking at the post, he saw dust falling from the ceiling, and as he turned to call the men to alert them to the possible damage, the ceiling with the boulder collapsed, creating a chain effect that collapsed the whole mine. The man was buried under the wooden ledge and the boulder had dropped on top of it at an angle that pinned him face forward into the ground. He was badly injured.

However, his injuries were nothing, as he remembered that the men were deeper in the mine, with bigger, heavier boulders protruding out of the walls and ceiling and the way the hole was dug in the ground, if it was to be blocked off and collapse, anyone working deep within would be crushed, and even if somehow they avoided being crushed, they would eventually suffocate from lack of air.

The man cried in the hospital, as he knew, all the men working deep in the mine could not survive.

The rescuers worked tirelessly through the night for three days straight. They used small pickaxes and rubble removers, cautiously removing debris and rubble in an attempt to save the men, buried deep within the mine. All the men who worked in the mine had been trained on how to prevent themselves from being crushed, should a collapse take place, so they had hoped that maybe the men were able to get into a cavity that prevented them from being crushed, and that hopefully, all they needed to do was to open a small pocket of air to allow the men to breathe until they could be rescued.

Sadly, after four days of digging, the rescuers finally got to the deeper part of the mine and discovered that the men had all been crushed by large rocks, as they fell on them, killing them all instantly.

After all the bodies were accounted for, a mass funeral service was held immediately for all the men who died, with Bill's father, Mr. Tackey amongst the dead. They buried all the bodies in the town cemetery the very next day. His wife tried her best to keep her composure throughout the funeral service, but upon arriving home, she broke down heavily, crying as she held onto Mary Lamb, who was also crying. Bill knew his mother was sad, so he cried as well.

After this, things began to be harder for Bill and his family.

When he was outside playing by himself with rocks and sticks, children would pelt him with small stones and cause him to scream out and cry. They called him names and instead of his initial nickname of *"Mackey"* that some of the now-deceased men had given him, they instead called him *"Suckey"* and another word I will not use here, as they substituted the "S" for the letter "F".

When Bill was walking outside, people stared at him and mumbled under their breaths, asking how their husbands are dead and this "retarded" boy was still alive. People were angry and sad, but rightfully so, as their husbands and brothers all perished in a mine collapse, that Bill himself had caused, all because he wanted to chase a rat, and couldn't control his anger.

Some people tried to remain nice and at least fair to Bill, for they understood that he was just a boy, who didn't ask to be born developmentally disabled. They would call him and give him small bags with fruit and bread to take home to his mother, who now had to find work along with some of the other mothers and wives, as their husbands were gone.

Bill would bring home the food, and give it to Mary Lamb, who dropped out of school for the year to help her mother at home with Bill and the household duties. She would help her mother cook for them and clean up as much as she could. Their lives had gotten harder, and to make matters worse, Bill could not even really be of much use to help out, even if they needed him to.

Even his mother grew slightly colder to Bill. She did not treat him harshly or yell at him. As a matter of fact, she stopped yelling at him altogether. She would instead look at him when he threw a tantrum and just walk away, leaving him to scream and cry until he calmed down. Before this, she would stay and talk to him and try to get him to calm down, but now, perhaps due to being tired and having more important things on her mind, she would just walk away and leave him alone.

Sometimes, she would be frustrated that he wanted to do something he shouldn't, like jump on the bed and risk breaking it, and when she told him not to do it, and he still did so, she would walk away from him, and when Bill saw that, he called for her, but she wouldn't answer, and when she didn't, he would get scared and run to her, and for a few seconds she would look at him and not answer. This scared Bill to no end, and he would cry and hold her clothes and shout *"Sorry!"* until she answered. At times she was sorry she did that to him, but she felt it was necessary to punish him when he was misbehaving, as he was a handful, and wanted to show him that she would not give him attention if he misbehaved.

She always spoke to him after a few moments however, and this simple treatment worked and taught Bill that she was serious when she got quiet, and he knew to stop misbehaving immediately.

His sister would still try to take care of him when she could, but she was careful of him and when he appeared to get upset, she would quickly walk away, to avoid getting shoved or hit by Bill.

* * * * *

Two years had passed, and Bill, now sixteen, was older and although still very much childish in many respects, had begun to stop throwing constant screaming tantrums, and was much quieter, but still destructive of things he got his hands on. He still had to be very much taken care of, by his Mother and Mary Lamb, but he was beginning to be able to go out for longer periods by himself, with little to no supervision.

The people in the town still disliked him, for they did not forget his crime against them, nor did many forgive him, but they began to refer to him once again as *"Bill Tackey, The Mackey"*, even though it was said in a sarcastic tone and essentially in an ironic way, and that although he had that nickname, he was in reality, the complete opposite of the word *"Mackey"*. Bill, of course, didn't realize this and answered to the name as normal.

Bill would often wonder about by himself, for hours on end, and only returned home for food or something to drink. He wandered farther and farther away, until soon, he had gone to the area of the mine, and began to play there by himself.

One day, whilst playing near the water, he saw another rat run out of his hole towards what used to be the entrance of the mine. It had now been dug out and boarded up, with small spaces between the wood.

His mother, along with several of the women in the town lobbied to have the mine destroyed for good, as it stood there as a monument to their dead husbands and didn't like that it sat there, boarded up and present, reminding them constantly of their loss. The town, however, refused to close the mine. So there it sat, lonely and empty.

Bill walked over to the entrance, now hesitant to chase the rat any further, as he remembered all the bad things that happened to him after he did it the first time, and stood in front of the boarded-up entrance, trying to peek inside, past the wood. He initially turned around to walk away when he thought he heard drops of water and then turned back around to investigate. There were drops of water, dripping in a hollow part in the mine, now more resembling a small cave.

Curiosity got the best of Bill, and he pulled away a small piece of wood, making a hole big enough for him to step into the mine. He then walked in, venturing deeper into the mine, listening to the sound of the dripping water.

Bill walked a few steps and heard the water drops getting stronger. He had the light of the entrance of the mine behind him, so he kept walking. As he reached the source of the water dripping, he looked further down and saw a small hole the water had worn away, just large enough for him to step into. He began to play and splash in the water, and as kids do when they see puddles, he began to slush and stomp in it. As he slushed around in the water, he made a big jump into the small puddle, and the ground, apparently unstable, began to give way, and Bill fell, into another small burrow in the ground, about five feet high, with small, sharp rocks and protruding glass all around the sides. It cut and scraped his legs and his arms. He got up and first tried to climb out, but he couldn't, as the pieces of glass and rocks were cutting him. He looked around him in the hole. Now realizing he was alone and trapped in a small hole in a dimly lit cave, he began to get scared and cried out for his mother, and for Mary Lamb. He then screamed, but as he heard his echo, it scared him and he got quiet.

His hands and arms were beginning to sting from the small cuts, so he started crying again, and now beginning to be panicked again, he scrambled as hard as he could, and successfully managed to climb out of the hole, with a tiny sharp piece of glass lodging itself in his hand.

Bill ran to the entrance of the cave as fast as he could, and passed through the boarded-up entrance, and ran home. As he ran, he looked at his bleeding hand and picked the small sharp piece of glass out of his hand. He looked at it, then threw it away as he cried, waving his bleeding hands all the way home.

Once he got close to home, Mary Lamb heard all the commotion, and went outside to meet her brother, crying and waving his arms as it stung from the cuts. She quickly washed his arms and legs, along with his hands, and applied some topical medicine they bought from the store for minor scrapes and bruises. Then she put small bandages on his cuts and bruises and tried to calm him down.

Later that afternoon, when their mother got home from her job in the market, Mary Lamb told their mother about what happened. Bill's mother inspected him all over, then asked Bill to tell her how he got hurt. Bill shouted out "Rat", then "Mine" and "Hole" and "Glass" as his mother asked him what happened next. He was feeling a little better after seeing her, so he relaxed some more and told her as much as he could.

Bill's mother told Bill that she hoped he learned his lesson and that he should never, ever go back to the mine again, or he might get hurt, and this time, no one would be able to save him.

* * * * *

Some time passed after this, and with his skin now healed, Bill once again, disobeying his mother, ventured to the mine. The mine was still blocked off at the entrance, with a wide enough hole to get through.

This time, Bill was smart. He brought a small flashlight his father kept in the house and stole it when his mother wasn't looking. He ventured into the mine, now, able to see, and walked to the back, looking for the same hole he fell in, to avoid it. As he got deep into the cave, he spotted the hole and went to walk around it, but something shiny caught his eye as the light bounced off the walls of the mine.

As Bill shined the light deeper at the hole, he saw bits of broken glass in the hole and some stuck on the walls where he had previously fallen, and it shone with the bright light of the flashlight. He got as close to the edge as he could and picked up a small piece and put it in his pocket for a souvenir to play with later. Mary had told him not to play with glass as he would get cut, but he brushed the idea away in his mind, as he felt she always tried to take away his things. He then walked past the hole and ventured deep into the mine.

Bill spent another half hour or so, exploring the mine, looking at all the black dust and coal everywhere. He stopped, as he remembered a spot where he would go into the mine with his father sometimes, and his father would make him wait in a corner, while he picked up supplies and other various things. The memory came back to Bill's mind, and he began to cry. He remembered *vividly* once again, that it was somehow because of him that his father was gone. Many of the townspeople had told him so, and they hated him for it.

This was more than what Bill could bear, and so he ran back to the entrance and left the mine, crying as he walked home.

When he got home, his mother noticed that he was crying and had black dust all over him, and asked Bill if he was at the cave again. He answered her.

This made his mother upset, and she asked him if he was hurt anywhere or if he had any cuts or stings. Bill answered no, then his mother scolded him and almost walked up to him as if to spank him, but she changed her mind and told Bill to take off his clothes so she could help him take a bath.

While Bill took his bath, his mother gathered up his clothes to add them to the laundry, and turned his pants legs inside out as most women do, and felt her hand get pricked by the sharp piece of glass Bill had left in his pocket. The prick drew a spot of blood on her finger, and she took out the piece of glass and looked at it. She then began to cry. She was not in pain from the prick, she was instead frustrated because Bill was not listening, as she knew that eventually, he would get hurt or even die, just as his father. She set the piece of glass on the shelf where her husband's toothbrush once sat and placed his clothes in the laundry basket.

The next day, as Bill's mother prepared for work, she saw the piece of glass on the shelf, and quickly picked it up to throw it away, lest Bill should see it and go to play with it and cut himself again, but instead got an idea to keep it as proof that leaving the mine as it was, was dangerous for children and people as the entrance was still open and available for all to still go inside.

Bill's mother, along with several other mothers, had in their grief and mourning, lobbied to have the mine destroyed, so no one could ever go there and open it again, or try to buy it out from the town. They had previously argued that their husbands had died there, and didn't want another accident like that, ever again. The town, however, having a small share in the mine, looked for potential buyers to buy out its share, as it was abandoned and not making any money, and as such, until then, the women couldn't legally have the mine destroyed.

As Bill's mother arrived at work, she went straight to one of her friends, who, along with her, had suffered a tragic loss when the mine collapsed. She had forgiven Bill a long time ago and was very close to his mother, who also, suffered a great loss that day. She brought the piece of glass to her friend and explained that they could use it as proof that the mine was dangerous, as who knows what leftover glass and broken machinery was still in there for curious kids and children to find, and that if it was a safety risk for their children and people venturing deep inside, they would have a stronger case to have it permanently closed.

Her friend agreed with her and told her that she knew of someone who worked in the town's charter, that was on their side and that they should go together to him that afternoon to make the case.

Later that afternoon, Bill's mother stopped home and saw Mary Lamb and Bill inside the house, eating a snack. She told Mary to prepare dinner after the snack and she headed with her friend to the town's charter, to meet her friend's friend.

Once there, they made their case to him and asked him to pull whatever strings he had to help their cause, and then Bill's mother pulled out the piece of glass and handed it to the man, as she said the mine was just too dangerous to keep it open, as her kid had found the glass, wandering around, and God knows what else was still leftover.

The man took the piece of glass in his hand and instantly told the mothers that this was a sharp piece of rock, not dirty glass. He said they couldn't use it as proof since it wasn't glass, and handed it back to Bill's mother. A man, sitting nearby, came over and upon seeing the piece of dirty rock, he asked Bill's mother to see it.

The man silently inspected the rock for about a minute then handed the piece of rock back to Bill's mother and asked her if she knew what that piece of *glass* was.

Bill's mother replied that she didn't know what it was because it looked like dirty glass.

The man laughed and replied that it was not glass by any means, and he would need tools to be 100% sure, but that it was in fact, burnished unpolished diamond.

* * * * *

There was a frenzy the next day in town. The mayor announced that something miraculous had been discovered in the old closed down mine and that they would be sending crews to examine the mine immediately. People began to get curious as to what it might be, and started gathering near the mine to get a glimpse of what was happening. Some people thought that instead of coal, perhaps salt was discovered in the walls. Little did they know the *salt* they were talking about, was in fact, burnished diamond, newly discovered in the mine.

The mayor spent the whole morning, consulting with lawyers and some of the town residents whose family owned a share of the mine, and then called a press conference, and invited a small camera crew from the neighboring town to come and film the announcement.

The mayor then spoke to the camera and announced that the mine was once inactive, but by some miracle, a small pocket of diamonds had been discovered in a small hole in the mine, with diggers possibly finding more tiny pockets.

The people began to get instantly excited and wanted to know more. Who had discovered it? Who now owned the mine? Would the town get rich from the diamonds?

The mayor falsely stated that it was one of his people that had discovered the diamonds in the mine, and as such, they would take the credit for the discovery.

This was of course false, as the true person who had discovered the diamonds was none other than Bill Tackey himself. The news was broadcast all over the surrounding area, and people from the town over, came in droves to see if they could buy property around the area, with the mayor denying all requests for land purchase until everything was sorted out.

The mayor called Bill's mother and explained why he said what he said. He said he did it for Bill's protection, and that Bill and his father would get a street named after him as a secret reward. His mother, who was opposed to the idea at first, initially agreed, because she knew that Bill was already a pariah in the town, and didn't want any extra attention on him as it was, as it was his fault that many people has lost their husbands, and so didn't feel it was right for him to now get the spotlight.

The town immediately began prospering from the sale of all the discovered diamonds, with all the families getting large compensation from their ownership shares from the mine. The town began to become more modern, catching up immediately with the surrounding towns, and increasing the town's worth. Bill, Mary, and their mother were able to move to a nice house and have a better life, now that Bill's mother didn't need to work anymore. Mary Lamb also went back to school and was able to successfully pass her entrance exams and enter college.

Life had now gotten better for Bill and his family.

As most of the town prospered, some who knew the truth, and saw the street named after Mr. Tackey and his son, Bill, they would come to his mother and thank her and congratulate Bill for improving everyone's lives. Some would cry combined tears of joy and sadness, as they realized that because of Bill, they lost their husbands and family members, but also because of that, they were able to discover such a treasure trove of diamonds, whereby, if the mine was still in operation, it would have been possible that the diamonds would never have been discovered, as the place Bill fell, was densely packed over with rocks prior to the mine collapsing, and that the collapse and subsequent digging and scraping, had unearthed the diamonds enough to be discovered.

These people, now when they saw Bill, referred to him as *"Bill Tackey, The Mackey"* once more, only now, with true purposeful meaning, for he had single-handedly destroyed and rebuilt the hope and wealth of the town, all on his own.

Bill Tackey, *The Mackey*, indeed.

Part II

The Fantastical Poems

"The curious thing that resides in this bottle, is a compunctuation of the manifestation,

Of magical power.

All supposified in delightful perturbations and natural healing designifications,

This very *hour*."

-From, *The Representation of Glee*

Introduction (The Fantastical Poems)

Poems are exquisite things, aren't they? What other medium can a person use to express the inner workings of their soul, pouring out their feelings through the choice of words they use, as they seek to relay those feelings for all to witness and absorb?

Truly then, a poem, like a song, is like a personal outcry of emotion, shaped in a tale you want to tell, whether through rhyme or standard verse, as you lay it all bare; your soul, your heart, your mind, and your consciousness.

Some people use poetry to express love. Many feel it is, in many ways, the *ultimate* expression of love. While I do understand this, I am not too much of a love-poem writer. I wrote a single poem for someone I care for, *back* in my first book, and that will probably be the only one, for now.

Besides, there are so many other emotions one can express with a poem. Should poems only be used to express love? Certainly not. I use my poems to express amusement and wonder, anger and frustration, happiness, and encouragement, and finally, sadness and questionings. This, I find are excellent ways to use a poem in addition to love.

Some venture to use poems for many sundry topics as well. Topics that are important to them. This too is an excellent way to use the medium of poetry.

Interestingly enough, I have come to see that quite a lot of young adolescent people use poems to express their love and heartbreak. *Shocking,* I know. For them, this is a wonderful way to express their unrequited love, their first loves, and to navigate their mental states as they venture through the hell that is puberty.

To many, including myself, writing out their feelings hidden behind vague meanings and metaphors can be quite therapeutic.

My poems are indeed therapeutic for me, in that once I write them, the emotion gets transferred from my mind where I felt it originally, to paper, where I can part with some of the presence of the reality of it, and instead, it can exist seemingly in perpetual suspended animation, waiting to ephemerally transfer its held emotions to people as they read it.

This is what I use my poems for. To sing a song of *therapy*; A song of emotional therapy.

Oh, and to tell the occasional sarcastic joke. Yeah, I do that too.

Poems by Me

The Representation of Glee

Gather ye, come hither around, Let us consider this
matter; A strange substance I found,
of unnatural obstenifications.
To which I propose you use this consistently and
preferably with zero obligations, to you.

These delightful prejorablations, all set here, for
your pontifications of wonderment, and joy,
I present to you the customer, with my wondrous
solidification of *The Representation of Glee*, to buy.

The curious thing that resides in this bottle, is a
compunctuation of the manifestation,
Of magical power.
All supposified in delightful perturbations and
natural healing designifications,
This very *hour.*

Lucky for you, I come bearing gifts of these
robustications and amazing discoverabilities yet
To be,
Ponder not the ramifications of these
machinations, for you can sinceretively and
majoritively, *Trust* me.

What? You ask me to demonstrate the
mistifications and herbonfied solitary
properi-fications of, this wondrous elixir?
Sure, as long as you understand that it wintificallly
and rotiferously gesticulates within the body,

As an ailment *fixer.*

Drink now, for I will throw in not one, but two
scien-tabulous and banti-stabulous bottles, all for
the price of one,
Drink now I say, for when you are fantastically and
demonstratifically done,

I will surreptitiously and meticulously throw in, for
your manner and all likely good,
A large bottle of this magical aromaticulous snake
oil, illustrubly kept, in this bottle of wood.

True Happiness

True happiness lies, not in fortune or *fame*,

But in the quiet peace of being unknown.

For if you get noticed, you'll get all the *blame,*

Now the public, your freedom, they own.

True happiness comes, not from a pile of *money*,

But from a little, here and there,

Just enough to afford a little bit of *honey*,

(in your tea)

Or to take your daughter, to the county fair.

True happiness awaits, just around the *bend*,

Of the U-shaped circle of life,

Because you realize no one cannot *defend*,

A happy man, with a happy wife.

True happiness begins,

when you arrive at the booth,

The end of the search for the gold-laden *path*,

Instead it comes, when you see the truth,

True happiness comes when you *laugh*. :.)

Life Is Rough

Life Is Rough, Work is hard, I get it.

Don't give up now, keep at it or else you'll regret it.

Push on through, be determined and fight it,

But keep your fingers close,

or the scary world may bite it,

Completely off.

Life Is Sad, I know, I feel you,

The acid of negative people will definitely peel you,

Straight to the bone, then cauterize and seal you,

Till you're nothing left, A simple clear see-through
Broken set of *useless* glass.

Life is Crazy, I definitely know it,
The sooner you rise above, you end up below it,
It makes no sense so sometimes you throw it,
And give up the good fight, in fear you show it
By relinquishing your power to bestow it,
And make your own *damn* luck.

Life is Bad, I truly see this,
Have some hope, don't let that be the impetus,
For the crux of this poem,
the core where the meat is,
You were honestly in bad shape from adulthood,
all the way back to a fetus,
Just like *everyone* else.

Life is Tough, That's why I said,

Don't give up now, or you might as well be dead,

Give the trees and plants some food,

in your cemetery bed,

At least you'll be useful...Or live on instead,

Make your life your own,

walk towards the future and tread,

Don't be afraid and give in to the dread,

And please, get out from under that desk

over your head.

It's pathetic.

How To Rhyme

First, you start with a simple basic line,

Then mix the words, as you seek to refine,

The meaning of the concept you sought to write,

Then you balance the verbs to make it contrite.

Mix in a little hyperbole and strengthen the core,

Don't forget your symbolism

and the simple metaphor.

Tell the story from the start of the narrative path,

It's not hard at all, it's really basic elementary math.

You are leading the reader down a journey of song,

It doesn't have to be lengthy;

it doesn't have to be long.

Make the words match the idea you want or desire,

Even if you rhyme two opposite words,

like water and fire.

The lines will be fun,

it will come out nice and good,

As long as you understand,

no wait, I meant, *understood.*

It's not hard to rhyme,

take for instance the word, "*Orange*",

Just make up something silly,

or use the noun, "Door hinge".

You only really need, the end of any given word,

Anything else, and you are making it *too* absurd.

Try to end with the point you first sought to make,

Let it come out of the oven,

like a freshly baked cake.

As it reaches the minds of people,

as they come to read,

Know that you did something good,

something good indeed.

Last but not least, ensure you end with a bang,

Or there will be no point to what you just sung,

no sorry, I meant *sang*.

The Scared Little Peanut

The scared little peanut was sad,

he was certainly in a bind and a rut,

For he was fearful for his shell to be cracked,

and for someone to take his nut.

"Please don't crack my shell!"

the frightened peanut said,

For my body contains two nuts, one at the lower,

and the other at the top of my head.

He thought about all the horrible things that could

happen to his poor, sensitive nuts,

It could be grinded, pushed and sucked on,

till there was nothing buts,

A shell of his former self, an open, empty bust,

He would save them at all cost, preserve his jewels,

he knew he must.

For he feared they would crack

and grind down on his nuts

Until it was good for nothing, no if's and's or but's,

How tired he would be,

the scared little peanut was sad,

For *no nut* would be left, no reward to be had.

The scared little peanut

began to search for his friends,

He wanted to see what they had to say

before his story ends.

He searched for his mates,

who like him shared a nut,

The nice green little Pistachio,

and the big brown Walnut.

Said the Walnut all proud,

whose shell was thick as a set,

"They can't crack me so easily,

that much I can bet!"

His shell was hard and brown, and very very firm,

He was glad to have his nuts eaten,

so this was a concern…

His friend, the pistachio was a girl it would seem,

for she loved nice little sprinkles of salt in between.

She was always soft and calm,

as she gave her advice to a fit,

As long as I stay cool, I'm ok,

but with heat I do split.

She told him about the truth,

she didn't hold back the good deed,

Of the story of the small little sunflower seed.

The sunflower seed was a nut,

but too small to be scared,

for he was so small to be used,

most people no longer cared.

His nut, he wanted to give,

as he was abundant, small and spry,

For some reason it seems, he simply didn't satisfy.

The scared little peanut left his friends in a huff,

he was more scared than before,

and for him it was rough.

He wasn't as big or as hard,

as the Walnut's thick shell,

Nor did he speak very softly,

like the stories the Pistachio could tell.

He was just a simple peanut,

a common nut to be known

All he wanted to do was to live,

Just long enough to become grown.

But a nut he was,

he couldn't escape the simple fact,

That his shell would one day be broken,

his nuts eaten, and that was that.

The Wonderland of Me

I'm not saying that I belong on a shelf,

That's not my place to be,

What I'm saying is that I'm simply *wonderful,*

That is, in the Wonderland of me.

A complex face, with emotional tastes,

A unique character, see?

I don't say this just to boast,

But I do it to some degree.

You'll see what I feel as you enter,

Into the Wonderland of me.

Enter my mind, you are sure to find,

There's a reason for my glee.

I choose to openly see the world,

With my own *unique* personality.

I offer you a chance to escape,

from your mundane reality,

That's what you'll find if you venture,

Into the Wonderland of me.

It's the only place you'll see,

The core of who I am,

and why I smile so happily!

This is how I wish to be.

You too can share this feeling,

When you come and join and see,

That is, if you choose to come visit,

My place, sincerely.

Come by, I will never charge to enter,

because it's simply free,

Remember, you chose amongst the rest,

To come and then *buy* me.

I would love to sit and talk with you

and drink a bit of tea,

All you have to do is come, and take a look and see,

Why it's so amazingly wonderful,

In the Wonderland of me.

Your Dreams

Your dreams are the hidden reality of your mind,
Stay there to live the treasures you seek to find.
Explore your world hidden deep within,
As broad as a universe, as minute as a pin.
Embrace your inner moment, learn who you are,
Start small and grow, then leap to your star.
Spend a little time there, and learn the truth,
Who cares if it's humble, bad, or uncouth?
Those dreams matter more than atoms abound,
It's there you will find hope,
there your happiness is found.
Then try to bring those dreams
to the top of the surface,
This is what gives you meaning, depth,

and life-long purpose.

Work towards them, then make them come to life,

Fight against all odds, negativity and strife.

One day you will see,

if you truly persevere and persist,

They will cease to be *just* dreams,

as now in *reality*, they'll exist.

That Time of Year, *Again*

Whispering willows, and wintery gusts,
Sleepy pillows, and pixie dust,
Sappy shades, and snowy soles,
Creeky blades, and bountiful bowls.

Noisy bells, and cantankerous pets,
Hidden wells, and China sets,
Gaudy gifts, and Clinky chimes,
Rocking rifts, and minty mimes.

Bustling bodies, and happy hearts,
Custardy cakes, and stinky farts.

Fanciful flowers, and baskety bits,
Titillating towers, and children's mits.

Manly manes, and musty mats,
Candy canes, and excessive fats,
Wintery weather and bitter cold,
It's that *time* of year again, it *never* gets old…

The Turd Between the Leaves

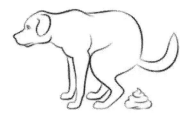

I once was trot-ting down the street,

And running through the breeze,

I tripped and fell upon my neck,

And tum-bled through the leaves.

(*Through the leaves.*)

I sprained my foot and bumped my back,

And screamed a big "oh geez!"

Won't some-one come and help me up,

I beg you, pret-ty please!

(*Pretty please!*)

Then sud-den-ly I got a smell,

Of something through the leaves,

A dog had left a little gift,

The one done after it pees.

(*After it pees.*)

I lay up-on my back and thought,

Just who do I appease?

For fate had seen it fit to track

The turd upon my knees.

(*Upon my knees.*)

But then I heard a prec-ious sound,

One that was sure to please,

It sound-ed like a person walked

Close-by beneath the trees.

(*Beneath the trees.*)

Yet to my hor-ror waiting still,

'Twas yet a sim-ple tease,

The dog had come right back to claim,

The place right where he pees.

(*Where he pees.*)

This dog was smart, he knew my lot,

He stood and watched the bees.

Instead to go and find some help,

He ignored my call-ing pleas.

(*My calling pleas.*)

My arms were numb, I couldn't move,

Like drown-ing in the seas,

This cru-el dog would use the chance,

To finish off his deeds.

(*Off his deeds.*)

He took one look upon my state,

He knew he had the keys,

To take revenge he sought of me,

To do just as he pleased.

(*As he pleased.*)

I once had chased him off you see,

I saw his brat-ty deeds,

He always bit upon a cat,

Would do so 'till it bleeds.

(*Till it bleeds.*)

Revenge had come, the dog was king,

It's funny how he sees,

The human down upon his back,

Now I will *pay* my fees.

(*Pay my fees.*)

The dog came close and sniffed my head,

Then walked just past the knees,

He lift-ed up his back right leg,

Released warm golden tea's.

(*Golden teas.*)

Once done, he scratched upon the spot,

Then turned to-wards the trees,

So proud of what he did to me,

He felt like Her-cu-les.

(*Hercules.*)

I got my arm to move again,

It was harder than you sees,

The autumn weather blew its cold,

The pee began to freeze.

(*Began to freeze.*)

Alas, I must be free from this,

Or I may catch disease,

The smell from pee and turds was strong,

And caused my lungs to wheeze.

(*Lungs to wheeze.*)

One day I'll get my chance to bring,

The ven-genance from these deeds,

Upon the dog who chose to gift,

The turd between the leaves.

(*Between the leaves.*)

A Double Sonnet of Two Stanza's (A Sonnet to break the Sonnet)

Is this something that can truly be done?

A double sonnet of two stanzas make?

Would that not simply be a lot of fun?

The traditional sonnet stanza break?

A double sonnet of two stanzas come,

Long overdue the length, too short I find,

To dismantle the old way to succumb,

To the thoughts truly going through my mind.

Yet I write in the original style,

To ensure to preserve the sonnet's fate,

If not, the poet society rile,

Of something that's new, I seek to create?

I write not a twice stanza'd sonnet 'til,

For yet, we hold to the old sonnet still.

Bonus Poems

Do Whatever Works for You

Do whatever works for you,

Simply because time never stops

to inquire if you did, Nor will it stop to ask you
why.

Do whatever works for you,

Your future is in your hands,

don't let it slip down the drain, or flush it down the
toilet, then cry.

Do whatever works for you,

If you don't do what you can,

then you cannot blame anyone but yourself,

Do whatever works for you,

Because in the future you will sigh,

When you see others happy, doing what works for
them, and no one else.

Do whatever works for you,

Ask yourself if you did the right thing

To save your miserable existence?

Do whatever works for you,

Simply because people don't really care,

They'll watch you and laugh, and still give you
resistance.

Do whatever works for you,

Life won't stop to ask you if you tried,

Nor will anyone stop to help you, they won't.

Do whatever works for you,

Simply because time never stops to inquire if you did,

Nor will it give a damn if you don't.

My Little Store

When you realize you are feeling utterly sad

and *completely* sore,

Please come to me, Come relax at my little store.

It's close nearby, just along the busy, gleeful shore,

Where the dolphins delight,

and the sea billows roar.

Come take the long drive, then take a little detour,

Don't be shy, come on in,

come and open my door.

A drink for you first, this for you I will pour,

For you are my guest,

there is nothing better I *wish* for.

Next I will greet you, then I will offer you a tour,

Of the wonderful things and delights,

that I sell in my store.

Of relaxing gadgets and gidgets

and plenty, plenty more,

Things you may have even seen,

but some never before.

I sell all sorts of things,

fanciful clothes you've never wore,

I sell gold-encrusted donuts, marshmellowy sheets,

and even platinum ore.

You will be fully excited!

For my items inspire great lore,

You will get goosebumps on your skin,

it will raise every pore.

You will be delighted!

Your mood and your mind will soar,

You will never get tired, lose interest or ever bore,

Of the happy things, the wondrous things,

the amazing things, or,

any of the beautiful and lovely things,

that I sell in my store.

So next time you are feeling pain,

Deep down in your core,

I would wish for you to come relax

and nothing more,

For I am always waiting here for you,

waiting here at my door,

Right here in my little shop,

yes, right here in my little store.

Part III

Author's Notes

Author's Notes (Short Stories)

The Amazing Choice

Back when I wrote *"The Amazing Opportunity"*, I envisioned the concept behind this story as well. *"The Amazing Choice"* was written as a direct continuation of *"The Amazing Opportunity"*. It continues right where our main character left off, after having undergone the experience with the prolific writer. The experience our main character goes through seems almost unreal…but maybe, just maybe it actually did happen? How bizarre would that be? I leave that for you to decide.

Weird Request Day

I love messing with people sometimes. *"Weird Request Day"* was written to quite frankly, mess with you. I wrote it along the vein of *"Office Blues"*, but at the same time, it is very different. Our main character in this instance is not *really* crazy or insane. Not at all. In this instance, almost everyone else around him might be. But don't get me wrong, our main character sees the world in a grossly distorted view, even slightly off reality. In fact, everyone in this story is a little messed up. *Everyone*. Oh, by the way,

I apologize for the ending. Don't be mad, ok? It's my little way of teasing you. Heck, if you ask nicely, I may even tell you what his boss asked. Hmm…maybe. We'll see.

The Bad Advice

I wanted to write a story this time, with you the reader, using your imagination and preconceived notions to interpret what you thought was the circumstances of the "ladies" in this story. I wrote it specifically so that you could run with one idea in your head: *These women work in a brothel and are clearly prostitutes*…But wait, they were *not*. I wanted to sum up the whole story in one last brief sentence. My goal then was to have you go back and read the story again, keeping in mind this new revelation. Changes things doesn't it? Now we see a wholly different scenario: Flowers competing for Bee pollination, not women looking to get together with men in a brothel. The older lady was the most mature flower; this is clearly why she was more attractive to all the "men" passing by, which were simply worker bees conducting their normal business. Strangely enough, you should ask yourself, how exactly is it any different between the two? That is, between women lurking and competing for men in a brothel or madam's house? These "ladies" are all *vying* for one promiscuous man to come and *get with them*. How nature any different than what women in brothels do? Makes you *think* huh? Nature is naaasty. :.)

Animals Unite

This is the final part of the tale of the *"Speech of Animals"* also featured in my first book. I at first, meant to leave the story as it was, somewhat finished as told in my first book, but seeing as to how I left things off, I knew I had to finish the tale, and give everyone the happy ending they deserved. I am not one for complete happy endings, as I feel a reader can suppose what comes after, but if ever a story I wrote needed completion, this one was it. If you haven't read *The Speech of Animals I and II*, please do, as this story is the final part, and it is an excellent story you don't want to miss.

The Chicken's Life

When I told my girlfriend that I was writing this story, a story about the true life of the chicken, she became very excited, and looked forward to reading it, as I would often tell her tales of my experiences growing up in the country, and living amongst the animals and seeing how their lives mirrored that of kings, warriors, and royalty. I would tell her jokes about how it was for me growing up around farm animals and the life they lived. I wrote this story meaning for it to be short and concise, but there was so much to tell, that I simply couldn't stay within the confines of a few thousand words. Seeing then, that I had so much to tell, I ended up telling the first part and leaving the second part for *"The Chicken's Life II"*. This first story deals more with the life of a hen, and the beginning of life for baby chicks.

The Chicken's Life II

"The Chicken's Life II" mostly deals with the struggles of our once famous rooster, Tito, who lived many years ago with us in the country. I told it through the lens of his life, but it is the same for all Roosters, as they are born, grow and struggle for dominance in the yard or confines of their simple, yet interesting lives. This whole story, from start to end is absolutely true, as many farmers and people who rear livestock can attest. Still yet, I hope you enjoy the tale of Tito, and appreciate the complexity and struggle for happiness of the simple yard fowls known to us as chickens, who are actually the *opposite* of what we portray in the common use of the word.

The Meeting

Simple coincidences happen in life. "The Meeting" is a short tale of such coincidences. In it, I briefly explore the value of life, what it means to care for something, and the concept that everything is special, and *everything and everyone* deserves to be saved. And you never know what your simple actions in life can do. Perhaps one day we may even find out together…

The Self-Help Guru

This story is an amusing tale of a slick young conman, named Mark. I initially wanted to go in a whole other direction than what it turned out to be, but when I started writing *"The Self-Help Guru"*, I couldn't help but follow where my thoughts led me. I had a lot of fun writing this one, and I hope you enjoy it. Besides, who doesn't like a good, old fashioned tale of trickery, jealousy, and deceit?

The Self-Help Guru II

I once again got carried away. I usually like to stay below three to four thousand words per short story as a rule if I can, but sadly, I keep breaking my own self-imposed maxims! This is the second part of the story and picks up right where the first part left off.

While writing, I make it a point never to examine or look at word count and only write according to how I feel, and the story I want to tell. This usually works out well for me. However, the entirety of *"The Self-Help Guru"* ended up being over ten thousand words! I simply had to break the story into two. It seems like this is somewhat of a pattern with me. When I'm editing and drafting how I want the stories to flow, I become fearful that I might have written too long of a story, and end up breaking them into separate parts. Perhaps I should start focusing on formatting my stories and marketing them as *novelettes*, as the word counts may be more suitable. Nonetheless, please enjoy this second and final part of the story of Mark and his effect on certain people in that small neighborhood.

The Decision

There can be happiness, even in our struggles, and yes, even in death. *"The Decision"* was written to portray the dramatic irony we sometimes face in this life. This story certainly ends sadly, but my focus with this story was to share with you the lesson, that in spite of what we are going through, if we just take a little time to accept the circumstances and embrace it, we might just find a small amount of self-healing happiness within it. It goes without saying, that experiencing something horrible or frightening can make it hard to do so, but as long as you have life, I urge you to cherish it. Remember, we only have but a small amount of time to live. It may be more than seconds, but we certainly won't live forever. Also, it is always wise to remember that whenever we feel we have it hard, there's probably someone experiencing something worse that you. Therefore, let us always embrace and be thankful for our happiness. Oh, and if possible, try to avoid doing dangerous things. Life is terrifying enough as it is, my friends. You can be just as happy riding a bike on a trail and find happiness. No need to do what our main character did, just to find happiness. Ok?

The Mocking of Bill Tackey, The Mackey

This story to me is so endearing. What people look at and think of as useless and worthless, ends up sometimes being the key to their later happiness. Sure, Bill caused a lot of pain and frustration, but at the end of it, because of his actions, everyone benefited and prospered. This is how it often goes in this life as well. It is important for us to always see the good in people. No matter what they look like, or what they might have done in the past. Of course, this is not always easy to do, but we should always try. *"The Mocking of Bill Tackey, The Mackey"* is a tale of unfortunate happenings, turned into happy events. The moral or lesson of this story is that sometimes, not always, but sometimes, we have to go through something *bad*, before we can get to the thing that's *good*.

Author's Notes (Poems)

The Representation of Glee

This poem is hilariously difficult! I love it though. This is one of my favorite poems in this book. If you were to attempt to perform this poem for others, you will quickly find it takes immense skill not to mess up the pronunciation of the words of this simple, *non-complicated* tale of the snake oil salesman. But tell me, do they not come as such, with wonderful pronouncements of incredible *prognostications* of wondrous properties, all inherent upon the belief that your happiness can be thus found in a bottle or perhaps, more modernly, in some *multi-step formula*? Perhaps we need to take a second look at our "self-help" gurus and prized motivational speakers…you know, since surely *their snake oil*…I meant…life advice works.

True Happiness

This is a simple poem I wrote to depict that our happiness can be derived from simple things, like going to the county fair with your children or having a good relationship with your wife or husband. Oftentimes we predicate our happiness on money and fame, which either runs out or leaves you for the next popular person. Instead, any activity where you can *laugh* and enjoy yourself is where happiness reigns.

Life Is Rough

I wanted to write a poem for the people who fear life and always seem to complain that it's tough. Well, yeah. It is. *"Life Is Rough"* was written to let those people know that you still gotta get up and do your thing. It's not easy, but you still gotta work. You gotta get out there and struggle. You gotta do the *electric boogie* and the life hustle thing, just like everyone else. No point in moping about it really. Plus, it's no excuse to stay home, and be lazy and complain that the system is against you. Get up off your ass and get it done. And, if you are out there, but scared to live and take risks, (safe risks) then get out from hiding under that proverbial "desk" and live. Live *damnit*. After all, we only get one crack at it. Don't waste it hiding.

How To Rhyme

I truly am a fan of the rhyme; it makes an otherwise dull sentence light up with sparkle and *lyrical* sound. Sure, I can write poetry that doesn't use a rhyming structure, but to me, that's too boring. I want my words to sing! I wrote *"How To Rhyme"* to show that it's fairly easy to do. I know some struggle with the medium itself, that is, to write poetry in such a manner, but in all honesty, you don't *always* have to rhyme. As long as you are expressing your true feelings, the words will come. They always do.

The Scared Little Peanut

Oh, the Children's poem. How I love them so much…So I wrote this poem as an amusing tale of the nut. Such a troubled nut he was! I wanted to try my hand at a nursery rhyme of sorts, although, it might be a long one for the kids to remember. That being said, yeah, read this one to your kids *very* carefully…as a matter of fact, maybe you shouldn't…

The Wonderland of Me

I love putting thoughts into inanimate objects. As a child, I always wondered if a certain item could think and talk, what would it say? What would the conversation be like? I wrote *"The Wonderland of Me"* as a cute little poem about a figurine or doll. As we know, dolls and toys bring so much happiness to children, and even to some adults as well. I imagine a doll being always happy and inviting, ever beckoning you to come and join it, as you enter their world to play with them. Indeed, many a childhood is marked by playing with their favorite doll or toy, as hours and hours of fun and happiness could be attributed to memories with them.

Your Dreams

I wrote *"Your Dreams"* to say that you should never give up on your dreams, no matter how difficult they are. If you persevere, you will eventually succeed, as long as your dreams don't involve harmful things to others. We often complain about how difficult it is to achieve our goals, but to me, the act of working towards them is what gives you purpose and gives your life meaning. And honestly, is this not what life is about? The ever-present quest to know your purpose and work towards or pursue your happiness?

That Time of Year, Again

Ah, Christmas. Isn't it a joyous time? The holiday season brings cheer to mostly everyone who celebrates *that time of year*. I wrote *"That Time of Year, Again"* to offer a *different* perspective. Amusingly then, I wanted to write a poem about those who do not thus like Christmas and the holiday season. The poem starts off merry enough, but quickly devolves into *not so good things*. Heheh. As for me, I like Christmas, so don't get me wrong, I just thought that the other perspective should be told. Not everyone looks forward to what the holiday brings…

The Turd Between The Leaves

I attest to you, this story absolutely happened. One hundred percent. I once fell, and as I lay there somewhat stunned, with dog turd on my legs, I got pee'd on by a vengeful dog. That's right. I admit it. I knew I needed to tell the tale, but I wasn't sure how. One day as I was browsing YouTube, listening to classical compositions, I came across *"The Pirates of Penzance"* and the famous piece: *"Sighing Softly to the River"* and I decided to use that as the structure and backdrop of my poem. I wrote

"The Turd Between The Leaves" to read and sound the same as *"Sighing Softly to the River"*. It fits perfectly! When you read it, try to sing it as the General did, with the pirates chiming in at the end of each stanza. It's absolutely hilarious.

A Double Sonnet of Two Stanza's (A Sonnet to break the Sonnet)

You know, I was always a person who went against the grain, *(figuratively speaking)* and it was always a lingering thought in my mind concerning certain poems. *Who even sets the rules to define how certain poems should be composed?* (Looking at you, oh *venerable* Haiku). Of particular interest, I always wondered about the Sonnet. I personally always admired the structure of the Sonnet as I studied it in literature class way back in high school, and admired it for its well defined and limited construction. Essentially, it is *fourteen lines of verse, with ten syllables making up each line. Then each line for the first twelve verses must follow an ABAB or ABBA rhyming scheme, with the last two lines rhyming together on the same AA or BB rhyming scheme.* Whew! Isn't that a lot to have to conform too? My goodness. It certainly is a complicated poetry structure. So…why shouldn't we break that? Or at least examine the possibility of loosening some of these restrictions? Why shouldn't we make it longer or shorter? Maybe, drop the syllable count? Eh? But alas, literary snobs, don't worry, what I wrote is still very much, a Sonnet. Fear not, for I too, share an appreciation for timeless, forgone tradition of times past. Thus, I wouldn't do that. So…just kidding ok? Lol. I don't want literary fanatics to have a heart attack. But, just to mess with you "poetic neat freaks", maybe I crept in an extra syllable within one of my lines…Oh, and *Mr. Haiku*, my friend, you're next…

Do Whatever Works For You

So yeah, this is my little pep-talk to all those who need it. *"Do Whatever Works For You"* is meant to let you know that while there are some people who generally care about you and your needs, that is, mostly your family and close friends, most people don't care. After all, why should they? They are doing whatever works for *them*. Thus you should always do whatever works for *you*. Think about it. Will time stop to say, *"Hey you, are you good? Did you do your thing? Ok cool, I can keep going now."* Of course, time won't, nor anyone else will stop to do that as well. Thus you should make sure you are always doing what works for you, and no one else. This is not to mean that you should be selfish, or that you shouldn't participate in, or abide by society's rules or structures, for example, you still have to go to work, and most times, it will be working *for* someone, at *their* company or business. However, despite this, make sure that whatever you do, you don't regret it later. It simply means that you should always strive for your happiness first, whatever it is, and then you can help others. Anything else, and you are essentially working towards someone *else's* happiness. Try to never be that person. Always do whatever it takes to achieve your happiness. *No matter what*, come what may.

My Little Store

This poem is also one of my favorites. I wrote *"My Little Store"* as a sweet little poem, beckoning you to share in my wonder and delight as I imagine the perfect little store, where the shopkeeper is delighted to have you, and you are treated as if you are the only guest in the world. Would that not be a fun place to visit? I wrote this poem solely to warm your heart and give you a calm and nice feeling of going to a place where you are wanted and loved. A place where the shopkeeper can't wait to see you, a place where you would be excited by all the amazing things you could buy. Emotionally speaking, we all have that desire to be treated as such. Even if you've never had this experience in real life, I hope you can read my words and derive a little bit of comfort and relaxation, as you imagine visiting this wonderful little place, that is, this wonderful *little store.*

Part IV

List of Pre-Story Epigraphs and Meanings Behind Them

Preamble:

So do you like my Epigraphs? I love writing them! They pair so well with the stories. If, when deciding to pick up my book to read a certain story, you just aren't sure what it will be about, just read the epigraph first and get a little taste as to what you will read about before diving in. But don't blame me, since they're designed to suck you in! For this second go-around of writing my own epigraphs, I focused a lot on giving a small glimpse into introducing each of my stories as plain and simple as possible. I do still like to use a riddle here or there though. This section is to help you understand some of the meanings behind them, that is, if you haven't already deduced them with your brilliant minds!

The Epigraphs

"A man makes a choice to venture for what he wants, but time plays tricks and offers cruel taunts. He will have to choose in this realistic state, for things are not as they seem, in this sudden twist of fate."

This Epigraph should tell you all you needed to know to dive into this story! After reading the story, did our main character make the right choice? Was time cruel? Does it all even matter? What would you do, given the chance?

"What is so uniquely weird, about the one strange thing of which you are paired? Or who, for the clean suck-able "Finger" actually cared?"

This Epigraph is one of my silliest. I wanted to prepare you for the nonsense I was going to thrust upon you in *"Weird Request Day"*. I even wanted to warn you that if you were to venture into this story, be prepared to see such epitomes as fingers needing to be sucked and such.

"What lieth within the heart of the beauty keep, a spoilt treasure to find, for it is not very deep; True beauty may be found, below the gleaming white surface, but to the root, you must dig, you must dig deep on purpose."

This Epigraph I wrote for *"The Bad Advice"* was a fun little riddle I came up with. I knew I wanted to create a riddle because I didn't want you to immediately figure out where I was going with the story, or in this case, what I was actually talking *about* in the story. I knew I needed to begin to lead the reader into thinking along the lines of shallow people who worked in *less than community approved* areas, who only see beauty as a way to win. The old adage rings true: "*Beauty is only skin deep.*" But in this case, my epigraph gave a small hint to what I was *truly* referring to. Not the heart, but the root…and in this case, quite *literally*.

"At last we reach the final tale, of human and beast interaction, will there be a chance to avenge the dog's untimely death, enough for animal satisfaction?"

If you haven't read *"The Speech of Animals I and II"* in my first book, you might be at a loss and wonder what this epigraph means? Heheh. You should go read *"The Speech of Animals"* in its entirety to find out. Trust me, you won't be disappointed.

"A story of bravery and one of care, the chicken is not an animal filled with fear. You may think as much from the commonly used word, but this is the true yard fowl's story, one you haven't heard."

I wrote this epigraph to allow you a glimpse into the story of the chicken. We often use the adjective *"chicken"* to describe someone who lacks courage and is fearful or scared. However, I attest to you now, these animals are not as "fearful" as you might think.

"A story of warriors and kings, the plot will grow and thicken, this is the final part of the tale, of the indomitable chicken."

I wrote this to let you know to be prepared! Be prepared for a tale of bravery and triumph. One of warriors and perseverance. *"The Chicken's Life II"* is a tale of comeuppance and victory. This epigraph seeks to prepare you for this second tale, and what comes next.

"You never know where your actions in life may lead, all you can do is follow your heart, follow your heart indeed."

I wanted to tell a short, sweet story, and I simply wanted to feature the core of the story within the epigraph to give you an idea of what the story will be about.

"Wits match with wit, jealousy and envy run high, he is popular, handsome, and rich, he makes the ladies gossip and sigh."

Juicy isn't it? This epigraph was written to provide you with a quick outline summary of what this story would be about. Combine that with the simple clipart I used for the representation of the story, you gotta admit, it at least made you a little bit curious to read it and find out where it goes…

"A gift wrapped in impressive paper does not make it true, sometimes we must look past the sparkle, for a clearer point of view. What we think is worth sacrificing our true happiness for, is simply a sham; for you throw your happiness out the door."

This epigraph also contains the *true* meaning behind *"The Self-Help Guru II"*. The crux or moral of the whole story being that we should be contented and happy with what we have. Also, don't be impressed with flashy people. Oftentimes, it's simply a sham, or worse yet, a scam.

"We sometimes look for grand experiences our happiness to shape, we even seek to fly, without a superhero's cape. When we realize the truth, and miss our one true calling, it's essentially too late, for we're already falling."

I must admit, *"The Decision"* was one of my more challenging stories to write. I have never gone skydiving, and as such I don't think I ever will, but I sat and envisioned what it would be like to fall...without a safety line. Scary! Just thinking about it is terrifying. Sometimes our quest for happiness takes us to the edge. Some people can come down from the ledge and see the truth. Some topple off. This epigraph was written to prepare you for a wild ride, or more accurately, one heck of a *fall*.

"If ever you feel someone is useless and not worth the trouble, come out of your small, self-aggrandizing bubble. For everyone has value, and a part to play, it may not be now, but you'll see it someday."

Does this not ring true in real life? People we cast away as worthless or bothersome, or those who have caused trouble or accidental pain to others as seen as no good and useless to society. This epigraph tells you that we shouldn't count out people like that. Yes, they have caused suffering and sometimes great pain, but they are still human. They are still one of us. We should give them a chance, and sometimes it could even lead to happiness down the line.

Glossary (Of made up words)

Bizniz – Business

Requexistence – Request Existence

Obstenifications – Unlimited or Unknown
Origins

Prejorablations – Things

Compunctuation – Ending Result

Supposified – Supposedly

Perturbations – Mechanics

Designifications – Designs

Robustications – Robust things

Sinceretively – Sincerely

Majoritively – Majorly

Mistifications – Mystical Properties

Herbonified – Herbal

Solitary Properifications – Sole or Core
Properties

Wintifically – In a Complex Manner

Rotiferously – Vociferous, Furious,

Furiously

Gesticulates – Works or Carries out its

Action

Scientabulous – Scientifically Fabulous

Bantistabulous – Generating a lot of

Conversation, Fabulously.

Demonstratifically – Meaningfully and

Clearly

Shown or Demonstrated

Aromaticulous – Aromatic

Illustribly – Pridefully

Epilogue: Until We Meet Once More

So, did you enjoy it? Did you laugh a little here and there? I truly hope you enjoyed my second book! It was very fun to write. While my first book, *"The Many Minds of Me"* was mostly a serious work, I wanted to relax this time, and expound on the concept of happiness and things to make light of.

Do I plan to write more? Yes! I want to start putting efforts into other literary works, perhaps this time, the Novel. But honestly, I don't know for sure, because I must say, I do love my short stories and poems. Tell you what, we'll see how it goes.

As before, I continue to be open to any and all critics (or compliments for saving your marriage) and I would love to continue to discuss insights and gain further knowledge from others who like me, only seek to entertain and give you a small escape from the troubles of this world.

I truly hope you laughed. But if you didn't, then maybe you need your funny bone checked.

Go on, check it. It's right there encased behind your ribs on your left side…

Contact me anytime: **kingsley.nurse1@gmail.com**

May you be blessed until we can meet once more.

Perhaps in a full poetry book, or maybe a novelette or a novella…or who knows, maybe a full three-book series, epic adventure…

We'll see how it goes.

As always, from my mind, *gleefully* to yours,

-Kingsley

P.S. If you haven't already, don't forget to check out my first book, which is the sister to this book. It's called: **"The Many Minds of Me: A Book of Short Stories and Poems for the World, from My Mind"**. It's my first published work, and it's a really good book. You should read it. :.)